Student comments from Lady's classes:

"Love, love, LOVE the notebook and its thoroughness. It allowed me to concentrate on listening and less note taking. I haven't had a chance to read the notebook, but it has excellent use of references, footnotes, and links to keep me busy for a while! Wonderful job of graphics and photos for the PowerPoint Presentations. Most of all, I enjoyed your delivery of the information. Good voice volume and slow speaking are awesome for the hearing impaired. I have been beekeeping and selling hive products for 10 years and am blown away by how much I learned! Lady is a storehouse of incredibly vital knowledge!" -J

"The course was very interesting and enjoyable. The instructor was very knowledgeable and answered many of my questions. I came here not knowing much about apitherapy and am going back with a lot of information. Will definitely recommend it to all my friends who are interested in this area." -GA

"When I went home last evening I was filled and excited with new knowledge and insight. You inspired me with your strength of conviction and love of bees. There is a very special connection with Mother Nature that radiated throughout your stories and information shared. Unquestionable credibility and joy of working with bees and bee sacraments was impressive. I feel privileged and honored to have been in your presence and introduced to Apitherapy. Course exceeded my expectations." –C

Lady's class was informative, educational, passionate, and inspiring. The size of the class allowed for intimacy and interaction between the students. I believe I have formed life bonding relationships in this class!" -G

"Thank you for a wonderful and educating weekend. So much information covered in a few days was amazing. I have been to conferences that lasted 5 days, yet never gathered the amount of usable information as I have here. Thank you and hope to see in the fall!" -P

"Thank you – I enjoyed meeting you and your Staff. I am so lucky to have joined your mini-gathering to learn of bees and apitherapy. Your aura is beautiful and you have inspired me to be a better bee guardian and person of this earth. Until we meet again." -C

"Thank you so much for the fun-filled, informative weekend. I have been so honored to have met you and be able to learn from you. I have so much information spinning around in my head. I can't wait to get back home to process everything. I hope to be able to take this information and continue on my journey helping, healing, and continuing to learn." -C

"I learned so much from Lady that I feel that it will help me with my bees and the apitherapy side. Lady has so much knowledge to share that one class is not enough." -T

"Your beekeeping class and apitherapy class were very informative, enlightening, and entertaining. Every second was fascinating and opened my mind and spirit to communication with bees and ways to help my family heal. Thank you for your patience with my questions and for sharing your kindness, knowledge, and gifts. I bee-lieve this has been a life-changing weekend."-D

Apitherapy

From a BEekeeper's Perspective

by

Lady Spirit Moon

Certified Beekeeper, Certified Nutritionist,
Master Herbalist, Certified Apitherapist
Ambassador Emeritus, Center for Honeybee Research

Peace Publishers

Apitherapy
From a BEekeeper's Perspective

Lady Spirit Moon, CB, CN, MH, CA

Copyright © 2016 Lady Cerelli

Book on file at the Library of Congress

ISBN: 978-0-9798883-1-1

Peace Publishers
443 West Rd.
Hot Spring, NC 28743
beehealing@gmail.com

Book design by Lady Spirit Moon

Printed in the USA

Acknowledgements

I wish to thank Papa, my husband, for his patience in taking me out for rides to help me rest from the keyboard. My close circle of friends who tolerated me and my occasional rantings when I was frustrated; Mother Earth for rejuvenating my burned out energy when I weeded the garden; my girls in the bee yard for my endless healing; and for those who supported me in all the ways a writer needs when she gets tired and on the verge of giving up. I also wish to thank Dr. Stephan Stangaciu for responding to my endless questions while taking his apitherapy course online at www.apitherapy.com. I extend my gratitude to Dr. Michael Simics for his lengthy explanation of bee venom and to Dr. Bradford Weeks for reaching out and encouraging me.

As in any beehive colony, everyone is united as one with the energy of all accomplishing something good, strong, and lasting.

DEDICATION

This book is dedicated to the honeybees, without which humans cannot survive.

TABLE OF CONTENTS

Introduction

I am first and foremost a beekeeper. This is where my passion and purpose lies in my place in this Universe and probably for the rest of my life. I have discovered that honeybees are not only the most important pollinator we have because they don't cross-pollinate, but that they are so close to human beings in physical needs, they are the "canary in the cave" when it comes to warning us about dangers in our environment and food. And they have been warning us for years by dying off in huge numbers around the world.

While keeping bees I am always mindful how I handle them, listening to the sounds of their buzzing, which have on occasion turned into music. I am a Master Herbalist and a Certified Nutritionist, and have done massage therapy. But through learning from Dr. Stephan Stangaciu's Internet Apitherapy Course at www.apitherapy.com, researching on other websites, reading, and a whole lot of hands-on experience, I have come to discover a healing art unlike any other.

In a learned art sometimes there comes a moment when it becomes a part of your being after it penetrates your soul. Art stops being the laying on of hands and becomes a thing of intuition because of what it is. Apitherapy is that kind of art because you are taking a product made by an animal so ancient, its knowledge and history surpasses the existence of humans. Honeybees have existed for millions and millions of years, and as they evolved down through the eons from a solitary bee to a colony, we have eventually been allowed to tap into their knowledge.

A honeybee is about the size of a human's fingernail. Yet, the products it makes in the beehive can cure just about anything in that human's body. Too much of bee venom can kill. Just the right amount can make a person live a very long, healthy life, and even save it.

I have been doing "clinical" with herbs since the very early 1980s, long before I ever heard of the word. I was good with herbs and helped those whom the doctors had given up on because there was nothing else available. Allopathic medicine is so limited in its choices and can be so lethal because it is geared toward the masses and not toward the individual. Apitherapy, as with herbs, is very individualized.

Apitherapy is the extension of herbology as the bees take nectar from the flowers and the medicinal properties in the flowers can pass into the nectar the bees turn into honey. The bees take resin from buds and bark to make propolis from the same trees we we use for natural medicine. The hive's 8 products, bee venom, honey, propolis, royal jelly, beebread, pollen, apilarnil, and beeswax can all be individualized for anyone at any age whether they are male or female. All products are anti-microbial, anti-viral, anti-bacterial, and anti-fungal. The products can be combined with herbs, other elixirs, or used alone very affectively and easily, yet the healing results are often deemed miraculous.

As we explore each hive product, you and I will learn what the honeybee needs to create that product; what part of their body is involved in each product; the life-cycle of the bee; how the product is used for personal health and well-being; and how to sustainably harvest the raw products from the hive.

The honeybee is the most important pollinator because it does not cross pollinate and is responsible for about 84% of your food. Right now they are in a global crisis. I pray that in your understanding of the sacrifices they make and what it takes for them to bring you the tiny healing miracles from their bodies, you will learn to honor these tiny ancient beings and put forth every effort to save them from extinction.

BEe loved,
Lady Spirit Moon
CB, CN, MH, CA

Chapter 1

Getting Started

Before Getting Your Bees:

Before you first get your bees you need to think about a few things. Folks will tell you that the hive entrance needs to face south or southeast. Fact is bees will go wherever they have space and there is a good chance of survival. Most often they will not be particular where they live when they swarm. I know of a swarm that survived in a black plastic bag for a couple of months before the young man put it into a hive.

If the entrance is facing south, they will feel the sun as it rises in the east and build more honey frames on the west side to protect against the heat of the setting sun. Understand, I can tell you these things, but honeybees don't know how to read and can often be notional. They don't always feel the need to follow normal bee behavior.

If you live in an area where there are bears or deer, you will need to surround your apiary with an electrified fence. Deer have given me the most problems. In an open field of no obstacles, they deliberately brushed up against the hive and knocked it over. You haven't seen angry bees until you upright a hive and put it back together.

When you do set up your apiary, be sure you have running room around the entire apiary and the fence. I would also suggest you don't set the hives alongside each other, but rather space the hives about 2' apart. On an 8' frame I have a hive, a shelf, 2 hives, a shelf, and another hive – 4 hives in all.

Get a mentor by joining a local bee club. There are plenty of members that will tell you what kind of clothing gear you need to wear and what kind of tools will fit your style of beekeeping. If you can, test try on the clothing before purchasing and ask to try out tools for ease of handling. And if at all possible, get a mentor and work in his/her yard before you get your bees. Bees can smell fear because of the hormone you emit. The more comfortable you are before working your own bees, the less they will die due to stinging and fumbling during inspection.

What the Bees Need as Food:

If you live in the woods, you are blessed. If you live in the woods and there is industry around you or a GMO farmer within 10 miles and no one uses any 'cides (insecticide, herbicide, or fungicide), you have found a heaven for you and your bees. They can find plenty of food and propolis among the trees and blossoms. If you have a lot of property and you want to help the bees out more, put in your own plants.

You can research online for the various plants you can grow for bees in your geographic area. What I do suggest is that you learn:

- Where to plant invasive or non-invasive plants.
- Plant only a few hybrids because bees are not fond of them.
- Learn companion planting. There are books out there. Companion planting demonstrates ways of maintaining your plants without using any of the 'cides.
- Plant as many different medicinal herbs as you can, including those like lavender, anise hyssop, catnip, garlic, comfrey, sage, mints, etc. *Thymus serpyllum*, the true Mother of Thyme, will help with Varroa.
- Get creative and grow aquatic plants in a pond away from the house. Sometimes mosquitos will grow in the pond so you don't want the pond where you sit to relax. Sometimes you can put Koi fish in the pond to help with the insects and algae. We had put 2" goldfish in a plastic-lined pond that was 6' wide and 3' deep in the center. They stopped feeding off what we gave them and fed off the algae. In the winter time they would hibernate during the freezes. The goldfish got up to nearly 8" before the pond leaked.
- Don't forget the fruit trees. Make them the old fashioned varieties rather than the modern hybrids. The fruit may be smaller but, oh my, the flavor is usually intense. Besides, who actually eats all the fruit on the trees?

- If you grow vegetables in containers or a garden, plant some of your annual herbs among them. They tend to feed each other or protect each other, like planting basil among your tomatoes.

By watching the bees you can tell which plants have the most nutrition or are medicinal. It may sometimes surprise you after you look up a wild plant. Also watch a bee when it approaches a flower for nectar. When a flower still has nectar, it will emit a subtle electrical charge. When a bee approaches it, there will be a tiny static between the bee and the flower. This tells the bee there is nectar. 90 Seconds after the bee takes the last nectar, the flower stops emitting the electrical charge. So if there is no electrical charge, the bee goes on to the next flower.

The reason the honeybee is the most important of all the over 8,000 pollinators in the world is that the honeybee does not cross pollinate. The bumble bee will go from flower to flower without regard to the plant species, as other pollinators do. The honeybee is very conscious of the plant species. When it has gathered the last pollen or nectar, it will go back to the hive and deposit its stores then clean up before going back out to forage again. The honeybee maintains the integrity of the plant species and makes sure that your squash is a squash and a watermelon is a watermelon. If an apple is not the apple shape and is gnarly, it was not pollinated by a honeybee.

What I Learned in the Beginning:

You forget some of the things you learned in a bee school, especially if is just a couple days. There are a few absolutes you learn over time:

- Honeybees' autoimmune system is 67%, at best. Do your best to keep them out of stress. Stress is the number one cause of bee illnesses, like cresting EFB (European Foulbrood).
- Bees don't like loud noises or sharp, quick movements.
- Don't stand in front of the hive. The bees don't like obstacles in front of the entrance when they are coming in for a landing and are heavy from a full load of their harvest.
- Don't go into the hive when it is cloudy or if you know it is going to rain. The bees can feel the air pressure and don't like having their roof open.
- Even on cloudy days the bees can forage. The sun's UV rays coming through gray clouds help the honeybees navigate to sites.

- The bees remember faces and voices.
- They can count to 3.
- They recognize basic symbols.
- They can see colors, except red, which looks gray to them.
- If you have bees that are usually gentle and they make a fuss when you open the hive, you need to get out. There are things going on inside that the bees feel are private, especially when a queen is hatching or has been mated.
- Listen to the noises the bees make when you are sitting alongside the hive or when you open it. After a while, you will recognize what is going on inside by the sounds you hear.
- No matter how many daughter queens you have in one apiary, each daughter hive will have its own personality.
- Sometimes you can have a queen and a daughter queen in the same hive.
- The bees teach patience.

What I have learned about Bee Venom Therapy (BVT) was due to an accident and my arrogance. When I first started working with my bees, I didn't think they would sting me if I was gentle. I love my bees; why would they sting me? Trying to put my first nuc (nucleus) into its permanent hive, I dropped a frame. Mercy! It seemed nearly all of them came at me. I put the nuc back together as fast as I could and left the yard. I had never been stung before but received 40 stings that day. The next morning I stayed in bed with a low-grade fever, achy muscles and joints and knew what caused it all.

I knew I had to deal with those bees. A couple days later I went back out the yard and put the 2 nucs into their permanent homes. All beekeepers have their stories and I have mine based on the one hive. Later, walking back to the house, I took the short cut and slid down the bank. When I landed at the bottom, I could tell by how my foot was laying that I had broken a bone. I would later learn at the VA Hospital that I had chipped my heel on the large bone, and had a spiral break in the small bone. This put me out of beekeeping and in the wheelchair for 2 months.

The hospital took x-rays every 2 weeks. At the end of 8 weeks the orthopedic surgeon kept going back and forth between x-rays. I finally asked him what was wrong. He responded, "I don't think all of these x-rays are yours."

"What do you mean?"

"The x-rays taken over 6 weeks ago look different from the ones taken today, which are showing less arthritis than in the first x-ray."

I had to smile. "That's called Bee Venom." I knew then what I had read about BVT was true because I had just been given proof.

In an astonished voice, "You mean it works?" the doctor asked.

"You are looking at the result of 40 stings when I dropped a frame 8 weeks ago."

I went online to check out BVT and thus my amazing entrance into the world of Apitherapy.

~

Before You Begin Apitherapy

It's important you understand the duties of the worker bee as she ages. This will help you to see what is happening when you go into the hive for your inspections. It will also help to determine when you can harvest hive products.

The different stages of a worker bee from laid egg to hatching and their time of service during a honeybee's life:

Age	Duties
1 – 2	Cleans cells and warms the brood nest.
3 – 5	Feeds older larvae with honey and pollen.
6 – 11	Feeds young larvae with royal jelly.
12 – 17	Produces wax and constructs comb, ripens honey.
18 – 21	Guards the hive entrance and ventilates the hive.
22+	Forages for nectar, pollen, propolis, and water.

Chapter 2

What is Apitherapy?

The word is pronounced *a·pi*·ther·a·py with a long a. It derives from *ˌāpiTHerəpē*, Latin therapīa (Greek therapeía) healing - noun, plural apitherapies and means the use of products derived from bees as medicine, including venom, wax, honey, pollen/beebread, propolis, and royal jelly.

Apitherapy is an ancient art of healing dating back before the time of Christ. People have been using beehive products and most times know it heals but don't understand why. It has only been in the past few years that there have been studies done on hive products.

The healing products in the hive are: beeswax, apilarnil (larvae), royal jelly, honey, bee pollen, bee bread, propolis, and bee venom. In each chapter we will explore what it takes to make the product, how it's made, and what part in the bee anatomy makes it. In order to know how to harvest the products sustainably, it is important to understand what is going on from the time the product is harvested, to its creation, to your collecting it, and to using it in making your own product. Along the way I will pepper throughout the book little bits and pieces of information about the honeybee. You will have pictures and instructions on how to make the products. Recipes will follow at the end of each product chapter.

~

Before we start, you need to know that apitherapy is not legal in the USA or in any of its affiliated countries. Nor is it illegal. Though there has been some progress with FDA, apitherapy hasn't been recognized as a healing modality, yet. So protect yourself: **In the USA never use the words cure/heal, medicine, or patient/client when performing apitherapy as it will indicate you are practicing medicine.** I use the term "friend" instead of patient/client when I perform apitherapy because folks fill out an 8-page personal history form before I see them. By the time we take the 3 hours to go over the questionnaire face-to-face, we have established a bond of trust and we become friends.

Never advertise you do apitherapy nor charge a fee, as this will also be construed as doing apitherapy business or practicing medicine. You can ask for love tokens or donations. If you are good and effective, word of mouth will be all that you will need. The only people I know who are Bee Venom Therapy (BVT) are licensed acupuncturists and licensed medical physicians.

But in this book, for the sake of it being read by practitioners and apitherapists, I will use the term patient. As with any healing modalities there are principles that should be followed. Apitherapy is no different.

I will make this statement one time only, so please read carefully.

NOTE: <u>**ALWAYS, ALWAYS TEST FOR ALLERGIES**</u> **BEFORE ADMINISTERING ANY OF THE BEEHIVE PRODUCTS. READ DIRECTIONS ON ANAPHYLACTIC SHOCK SYMPTOMS AND HOW TO USE AN EPIPIN. IF IT IS CAUSED BY BEE VENOM ALLERGY, IMMEDIATELY FLICK THE STINGER OUT WITH FINGERNAIL AND USE THE EPIPEN. IN THE BVT SECTION, YOU WILL SEE WHAT MILD, INTERMEDITAE, AND SEVERE REACTIONS TO BEE VENOM LOOK LIKE AND HAVE THE INFORMATION FOR WHAT TO DO FOR THEM.**

Before doing any BVT, it is strongly suggested that you detox your body through herbal cleansing for at least 2 weeks to 30 days for your entire digestive tract which includes small and large intestines, liver, gallbladder. This should also detox your kidneys, lymph system, and blood circulating systems. All of these systems, especially large colon, are what feed your body. Folks rarely realize how sluggish their systems are due to the "junk" from their diets, air pollution, and medications. The blood slows down and sometimes bee venom has a hard time traveling through the blood vessels.

I have a friend who had severe reactions when he was stung by a wasp. He stayed swollen for weeks and carried the sting mark for just as long. I asked him to do a test for me, which included him just detoxing with herbal supplements for 30 days. First, I gave him a micro sting on his wrist to see what kind of reaction he would get. He swelled all the way up to his elbow.

He had already been eating an organic diet and stayed on it during the entire 30 days. He also took charcoal, Slippery Elm Bark twice a day, and Red Clover Blossoms. Slippery Elm Bark encapsulates anything that doesn't belong in the bowels and moves it out. It is also as nutritious as oatmeal. Red Clover Blossoms is the strongest blood cleanser in the herbal realm.

30 Days later, I gave him a full sting near the original micro sting. His hand nearly doubled in size over 3-4 days and just past the wrist. Then the swelling went down and all signs were gone in 10 days. This was a dramatic improvement overall. If you are thinking he got used to the venom because of the micro sting 30 days before, you should know that once a BVT program is started, you cannot miss a session, especially with Lyme disease. If you go more than 30 days, you have to start over because there is no venom left in your system.

I also suggest massage therapy, yoga, a nutritionist, Tai Chi...anything to give you balance and a good blood flow and movement throughout your body to relax it. Treat it as a sacred temple into which you continually go to discern its state of being.

Be patient. Natural products take time to be introduced into the body. Use beehive products with intent, and listen to your body. You cannot rush the body as it has its own time and rhythm for healing. If you push it you will harm yourself and most often risk setting back the healing process.

Chapter 3

Beeswax

What is Beeswax?

It takes about 8-10 pounds of honey for the bees to make 1 pound of beeswax.

Worker bees 12-17 days old use their wax glands to convert sugar into a waxy substance. This wax is secreted from 4 pairs of wax glands under the abdomen and it takes about 8-10 pounds of honey to make 1 pound of wax. The bees use their mandibles to manipulate the wax for comb and sealing. Photo: Backyardhive.com

"Beeswax, originally believed to have been collected from flowers or made from pollen, was discovered in 1744 by H.C. Hornbostel to be synthesized by four pairs of wax-secreting epidermal glands on the ventral side of worker abdomens. Only four natural resources (pollen, nectar, water, and plant resins known as propolis) are necessary to support all the colony's activities. Floral and extrafloral sugars (derived from phloem sap in the case of honeydew) are converted into the energetically expensive commodity we know as beeswax.

"Beeswax is produced by quiescent bees about 14 days old and worked into intricate complex double-sided hexagonal comb nest architectures that have allowed all the members of the true honey bee genus *Apis* to become the preeminent floral foragers of the insect world. Beeswax was probably a major factor in their evolution to the pinnacle of the eusocial insects. Eusocial means "living in a cooperative group in which usually one female and several males are reproductively active and the nonbreeding individuals care for the young or protect and provide for the group." Beeswax is extremely valuable to bees because much nectar and/or honey is "forfeited", that is lost as potential food and converted into structural material from the colony's annual energy budget to produce the wax combs. For this reason, beeswax is removed, reshaped, molded and used over and over again within the nest. The combs are literally the nursery, walls, storage pantry, home, pharmacy, and dance floor for the colony's myriad of occupants. Without their wax-secreting abilities evolved millions of years ago, honey bees would be largely unrecognizable to us."[1]

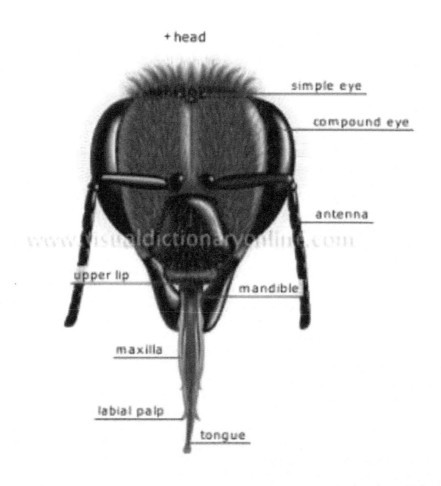

Bees use their front legs to grasp the wax from their abdomens after the wax is secreted then, use their mandibles to mold and reshape the wax.

Photo: Eric Tourneret

---

[1] *The Hive and the Honeybee*, 1992

What Beeswax Is Used for

Beeswax has been used for centuries for candles. It is smokeless, burns cleaner than paraffin wax, and lasts longer.

Beeswax has been used:

- To coat equipment for protection from humidity and rust;
- In cosmetics. A beekeeper in the Arizona desert sells his beeswax to a cosmetic company for a very large price as he is a chemical-free beekeeper.
- As bandages.
- Natural chewing gum.
- In healing balms.
- Ointments and salves to rejuvenate and grow skin because it contains:[2]
  - Hydrocarbons - 14%
  - Monoesters – 35%
  - Diesters – 14%
  - Triesters - 3%
  - Hydroxy monoesters – 4%
  - Hydroxy polyesters – 8%
  - Acid esters – 1%
  - Acid polyesters – 2%
  - Free acids – 12%
  - Free alcohols – 1%
  - Unidentified – 6%
- As a thickening agent for oils.

Is very stable a will not be affected by time.

Beeswax has one of the highest melting points of natural waxes, 62.8-65.6°C/145 – 150°F.

The thing to remember about beeswax is that it is non-polar and is not soluble in water without an emulsifier.

When beeswax is first secreted by the honeybees, they use the wax to create the foundation for brood and honey. The wax starts out white until

---

[2] *The Hive and the Honeybee, 1992, pg. 964*

what little pollen is in the honey turns the waxcomb to different shades of yellow. White beeswax is also used to cap honey on brood frames.

Wax Color

Over time the wax changes from white to brown to black because of the propolis that has been added to it, especially the brood cells. Each time a bee hatches, the worker bees don't clean the cells but coat them with propolis and wax. As yet, no one has been able to separate the layers of the brood cells. Even melting the wax in a pan or in a solar melter, the beekeeper finds that the cells come out as if someone had cut them out of the frame.

Comb properties change too as the cells become smaller, cell walls thicker, resulting in smaller bees. The walls can become so thick the bees on one end of the frame can hear what is going on the other end by feeling the resonation in the comb when the bees dance on the cell.

In the table below the gen column means the number of generations of bees. Taking into consideration the 21 days from egg to hatching of workers, there are 17 generations in a 365-year cycle. Chart[3]

Gen.	Comb color	Cell Volume cm3	Comb Thick. mm	Cell Dia. mm	Bee Mass mg	% Wax
0-1	yellow	0.282	0.22	5.42	123	86-100
2-5	brown	0.269	0.40	5.26	120	60
6-10	dark-brown	0.255	0.73	5.24	118	49
13-15	black	0.249	1.08	5.21	106	46

Cells measuring 4.9mm are the size of African (*Scutellata*) bees and are usually considered the best size as it is said that the cells are capped off sooner, thereby controlling the Varroa *destructor.* If the cells are larger than 5.0mm, it takes longer to seal the combs giving Varroa more chances to lay their eggs in the cell. If the bees measure smaller than 4.7mm they start to become ill and often are unable to generate enough heat in the cluster in the winter time, which is another reason to change out your frames.

---

[3] www.bee-hexagon.net

Each year beekeepers should stimulate bees into building new combs by discarding old combs out of the hive and replacing with at least 2-3 foundationless frames per colony. Brood combs should be exchanged at an interval of about 2-3 years. Some say 5 years.

Old dark combs:

- Are sources of infections.
- Can contaminate the stored honey with dirt particles, which is why you should not be harvesting honey for human consumption from these combs.
- Dark combs will also crystallize more readily in old combs, making hibernating more difficult.
- And old combs contain less wax as propolis is added after each hatching and with the larvae casings left behind will add more protein and will be more readily attacked by the wax moth.

Cleaning Wax

If you are a purist, there are wax brightening and bleaching acids. Do not mix the chemicals if you don't know what kind of reaction the combination will have on the environment. Always were special gloves designed for acids. They can be purchased at your local hardware stores or lab equipment companies. I haven't used any bleaching agents, either, but the following are some of the chemicals you can use:

- Acids - will bind a part of the iron which is responsible for wax darkening. Also they help to break emulsions and settle impurities. i.e., add 2-3 g concentrated citric acid or oxalic acid, or 1 ml concentrated sulfuric acid to 1 liter of water per kg wax and (add acid to water and not water to acid).

    If wax has a crumbly structure, it is due to wax saponification. You can revert this by adding soft water/rain water with sulfuric or oxalic acid to the wax and boil it. Water with a low mineral content should be used if such problems arise. However, in some cases, water/wax emulsions can occur, even with soft water. In such cases, raw molten wax in contact with water should be kept below 90°C (194°F).

Wax darkening - Don't use high heat for too long as it may damage the wax and darken its color. Wax should be heated in double boilers and not in reactive containers like iron, zinc brass, or copper vessels because these metals make the wax turn dark. Do not use lead containers because of contamination. Stainless steel or aluminum, is okay, but can be attacked by oxalic acid. Glass and enamel coated pans are the best to use.

- Hydrogen peroxide solution - add concentrated hydrogen peroxide solution (about 35 % in basic environment) to hot wax (100°C (212°F)). It is essential that the peroxide is used up in the bleaching process, as excess peroxide could cause problems in the manufacture of creams and ointments.

- Sun bleaching – a solar extractor will lighten the color of the wax. In order to achieve bleaching, the wax should be exposed to the sun for several days. Using a solar wax melter to melt the comb will give you a more natural colored comb.

- Potassium permanganate - heat wax at about 90°C (194°F) for 30 minutes in 0.01 % potassium permanganate in slightly acidic milieu. Exchange solution with water.

- Heated wax will have an odor if the honeycombs held fermented honey.

- Heat-resistant spores of *Paenibacillus larvae* (AFB) larvae are not killed by boiling wax in water. Only heating under pressure (1400 hPa) at 120°C (248°F) for 30 minutes will kill all spores.[4]

- Water-wax emulsions:
  - The wax-water appears milky, due to the presence of calcium or iron in the water Use 2-3 g of oxalic acid per kg wax and 1 ml of water to bind calcium, prevent emulsion, and to brighten wax at the same time.
  - Wax absorbs a great amount of water: heat wax at 105°C (221°F) to remove water.

---

[4] Machova, M (1993) ce of bacillus-larvae in beeswax. Apidologie 24 (1): 25-31

- Water is often incorporated in the process of wax manufacturing. Surplus water can be removed by heating at about 105°C (221°F). Prevent foam from building with defoaming agents, like silicon. The wax is free of water when there are no more bubbles.

- After melting, the wax is not pure enough. For additional cleaning use hot water tanks made from high-grade steel. The wax should stay in the water bath for a longer time at a temperature of 75-80°C (167°F-176°F), best overnight. Since wax is lighter than water, it floats. The dirt settles to the lower part of the wax, it must be scraped off after cooling. Under industrial conditions liquid wax can be cleaned by filtration with heated chamber filters. Wax can also be purified by hot filtration.

   NOTE: I have not used any of the above chemicals. If working with any of them, use protective gloves, goggles, and protective clothing.

If you decide to purchase the wax: Check for the expiration date of the commercial beeswax products and check if the beeswax comes from an organic apiary. Beeswax with chemical residues may bring on adverse reactions, especially in cosmetics.

Store beeswax in a dark cool place as it may contain some of the same elements that are in the nectar; and floral elements are destroyed by heat and light.

When heating wax, use a double boiler hot enough only to melt the wax. Too much of a heat will darken the wax.

Extracting Wax

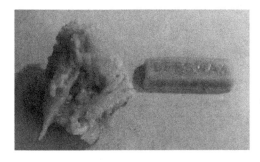

In the picture to the left, the wax on left was melted in a Solar Wax Melter, which separates the particles, but may still have honey in it. The wax bar on the right is wax taken from frames of combs that had been melted in a pot of water on a hot plate in a stainless pan. The entire comb with propolis, pollen, etc. was used, heated then strained. As you can see, the wax became darker because it took on some of the resin in the propolis and possibly, too, because the heat was too high.

For the homeowner, a Solar Wax Melter is the most economical way of melting wax and leaving the impurities behind on the shelf in the melter. Placing the melted wax in a pan of hot water and slowly melting it, stirring it occasionally to separate any more possible particles including the honey, will give you a cleaner wax for your cosmetics or for whatever else you might be using it.

My son built my wax melter according to the plan on http://www.BeeSource.com. It needs a little adapting as the container in front is too close to the pan above. But you can also make your own at home with equipment you have around the house. [5]

You will need:

- Styrofoam cooler or regular cooler
- Aluminum foil
- Paper towel
- Rubber bands
- Water
- Sheet of glass or Plexiglas

This is what your wax melter will look like once you complete the project.

Line the bottom and sides of the cooler. Put an inch of water in a plastic container that is about 4-6" high. Place a paper towel over top and wrap a rubber band around the towel so that the rubber band fits under the lid, or you can tightly tie a string around the lid. Trim the paper towel to about 1/2" below the rubber band. Place your wax on top. Put the glass on top of cooler.

[5] http://curbstonevalley.com/blog/?p=10333

Once the wax has melted it will leave slum gum (propolis-lined larvae cells) on top of the paper towel. You will not be able to separate this. It has been tried by scientists without success.

It will only take a few hours of a very hot sunny day to melt the wax. Once melted, let it cool if it is still hot. Lightly tap one corner of the wax and tip the container to drain the water out. Often you can just lift the wax out.

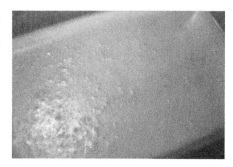

This is the color of your wax. Any wax that spilled in the cooler on the aluminum foil can be remelted.

You can remelt the wax and put into oil-lined 1 ounce plastic molds.

~

Recipes and Formulas

When making formulas keep in mind the polarity of the product. Honey is polar – water soluble; beeswax is non-polar – will not mix with water. For non-polar and polar products to mix, you will need an emulsifier like lecithin, glycerin, honey, egg yolk, soybeans, or mustard (seeds ground to paste).

Measurement conversions for beeswax

1 Tbsp.	=	½ ounce
2 Tbsp.	=	1 ounce
¼ C (4 Tbsp.)	=	2 ounces
½ C (8 Tbsp.)	=	4 ounces (¼ pound)
1 C (16 Tbsp.)	=	8 ounces (½ pound)
2 C (32 Tbsp.)	=	16 ounces (1 pound)

1. Dipped Pine Cones

   Dip pine cones half way in beeswax and set on wax paper to cool. These can be wrapped in see-thru wrappers with a red bow. These can be given as gifts for fire starters with added instructions to toss on the wood in the fireplace or campfire and set a match to the paper. I have sold them for $4.50.

2. Dipped Candles[6]

   Candle-making suppliers sell frames to make dipped candles, but a few dipped candles can be made without special equipment.

   a. Choose a container for the wax that is tall and thin so that the entire length of the candle can be dipped. Use 24-ply, flat-braid wicks for candles up to one-inch in diameter.
   b. Make a double boiler by placing the can in a pot and by placing wooden strips beneath the can to raise it an inch or so from the bottom.
   c. Add wax to the can and add water to the pot. Heat the wax to between 155-165°F. Place the wick in the wax and allow it to soak for about 5 minutes.
   d. Remove the wick, straighten it and TIE a weight to the end. Dip the wick into the wax and immediately remove it in a smooth motion. The wick should be dipped to the top of the candle each time and allowed a minute (or more) to cool between dips. Continue the dipping process until the candle is a little larger than a pencil. Clip the wick at the base to remove the weight and to flatten the base of the candle. Continue dipping until the candle is the desired diameter. A 3/4" diameter candle will require about 25 dips.
   e. Cut the base of the candle flat and dip it one or two more times to finish it. A small drip of wax should remain on the base. This is attractive and a trademark of hand-dipped candles.

   Note: Be careful that your pot for water is not a lot larger than the can of beeswax. You don't want the wax can to be floating around. The flashpoint of wax is 204°F and water boils at 212°F. Never turn you

---

[6] http://www.beeswaxfrombeekeepers.com/beeswaxrecipes.html

back on melting wax. If the wax catches fire, extinguish it with baking soda or, if you can, put a lid on it to smother the flames.

3. Warm Wax Treatment

Warm wax treatments are approved by the Arthritis Foundation to help relieve sore, painful joints caused by arthritis. Wax treatments provide moist heat, increased blood circulation, and ease stiffness due to joint inflammation.

5 pounds wax
2 cups mineral oil

Melt the ingredients in an oven set between 170-200 degrees F. Stir to mix the oil and wax. Remove the mixture from the oven and allow it to cool until there is a film of cooled wax on the surface (about 125 degrees F.) Test the wax to be sure it is very warm, but not uncomfortable.

For personal use the body part treated must be clean and dry. Dip the body part into the wax mixture and withdraw it. If the hand is being treated, wear disposable gloves to keep the fingers apart. Dip the hand into the wax a few more times until there is a thick coating of wax. When the heat is gone remove the gloves and put the wax back into the wax container.

If it is for an elbow or other part of the body, cover the body part with a plastic bag, and dip the elbow until the wax cools. If you can't dip the body part, paint the wax on with a spatula or stiff paint brush. When the wax has cooled, put what wax you can back into the wax container to use again. The treatment may be repeated. The mixture will melt more quickly now that the oil and wax are combined.

4. Waterproofing leather

¼ cup lanolin
2 Tablespoons beeswax
2 Tablespoons petroleum jelly

Combine the ingredients and melt them in a microwave or a double boiler. Brush the warm mixture over leather. Let this stand for a few hours and polish it with a cloth to remove excess waterproofing.

5. Archery Wax

1 ounce Beeswax
1 teaspoon rosin or cleaned propolis scrapings
This slightly sticky wax holds bow strings together. Melt the ingredients in a microwave or in a small can placed in boiling water. Pour the beeswax into a mold (muffin tin works well)* and let it cool. Rub bow strings with the block of wax so that heat is generated and the wax adheres.

*Note: Use wax paper to line the muffin tin cups. Peel off when needed.

6. Cheese Wax

After the air-drying period, when the cheese has developed a hard, dry rind, it must be protected with wax to prevent mold and further drying.

13.5 ounces beeswax
2.5 ounces vegetable shortening

For some cheeses you may want to add a Tbsp of Apple Cider Vinegar to help prevent mold.

Heat the ingredients in an oven at 200° F. until combined. Remove the wax from the oven and wait for it to reach 160-180°F. Dip the cheese and remove it with one quick, smooth motion. Repeat this step until the wax is about 1/16th inch thick.

7. Suppositories/Boluses

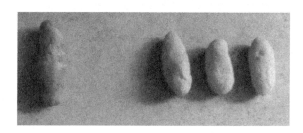

1 oz. beeswax
1 oz. coconut oil

Melt beeswax and coconut oil together in a double boiler. After melting and using a table spoon, pour a dollop of the mixture onto a wax coated paper or parchment paper. Allow to slightly cool, the wax will start changing its color. Then add 1 drop of Tea Tree oil onto each vaginal boluses (in photo on right); or add 1 tsp of Slippery Elm Bark Pdr. for suppositories (in photo on left). Knead until thoroughly mixed and roll into small finger-size boluses/suppositories in plastic wrap. Put in refrigerator until ready to use. (Lady's recipe)

8. Lip Balm

Keep your lips moisturized during winter months with this natural protectant.

Add ½ ounce (1 Tbsp) of beeswax to a small double boiler and melt on low heat. Add:

1 teaspoon of raw honey
2 ounces (4 Tbsp) of cold pressed organic olive oil
2 ounces (4 Tbsp) of cold pressed organic hemp seed oil

Stir for 1 to 2 minutes. For a little flavor, add about 20 drops of organic peppermint oil and stir well. Remove from heat and store in lip balm tins. (Honey in this recipe is used for sweetness. Heat over 94° will destroy some properties of honey.)

9. Skin Moisturizer

Lock in your skin's natural moisture with beeswax, and add the antioxidant vitamin E to help protect and repair rough, dry, or chapped skin. Melt in a double boiler:

4 ounces of sweet organic almond oil
1 ounce of beeswax

Remove from the heat and add 2 ounces of distilled water, stir well. Add 10 drops of vitamin E oil, 10 drops of lavender essential oil, and stir continuously until the mixture has cooled. Pour into individual tins.

10 Non-petroleum Jelly - Useful for making ointments.

1 ounce beeswax
1/2 cup sweet almond or olive oil

In a double boiler, melt the beeswax in the oil then pour into suitable container and allow it to set up. Mix the non-petroleum jelly with herb-infused oil or a powdered herb to make an ointment. Suggestions: Mix with Ginger Root Powder and spread on the chest for bronchitis. Mix with Green Tea Powder for an anti-wrinkle treatment.

SPECIAL NOTE: There 2 secrets behind mixing oil and liquids. First is an emulsifier like lecithin, liquid or dry, mixed in the ingredients. The second secret is heat. My Vita-mix allows me to keep the heat constant while it blends the ingredients - a form of homogenizing.

11 Itch Relief [7]

You can make a salve that's great for poison ivy, poison oak, and other itch causing adversaries. In a small saucepan and for 3 hours, simmer:

1 tablespoon of chickweed powder
1 tablespoon of comfrey power
1 pint of organic olive oil

Strain, add 2 ounces of beeswax, and pour into individual tins.

12 Plantain Salve for Stings[8]

1 cup olive oil or organic coconut oil
¼ cup beeswax
2 to 4 cups fresh plantain leaves or 2/3 to 1 1/3 cups dried plantain leaves that can be purchased at the bulk herb store.
5 to 10 drops of oil: Lavender, Purification, Frankincense, Tsuga, Balsam Fir to name a few. Tea tree – antimicrobial and antiviral;   Peppermint – pain reliever; Helichrysum (immortelle) – stops bleeding and analgesic; and Goldenseal oil or glyceride – antibiotic, anti-inflammatory.

---

[7] http://www.globalhealingcenter.com/natural-health/beeswax/
[8] https://sites.google.com/site/gratitude4health/home/young-living-essential-oils

Glass containers for the salve

Pour 1 cup of olive or coconut oil into a glass bowl and heat in a saucepan (like a double-boiler). Simmer over medium heat. Add the plantain leaves (a big handful of fresh CLEAN leaves, you can adjust your recipe or use 1/3 of that amount of dehydrated leaves). When it begins to simmer, remove it from the burner, cover, and let steep for about 30 minutes. Make sure that the plantain leaves are fully covered by the olive/coconut oil while steeping.

While that is steeping, grate 1/4 cup of beeswax or use beeswax pellets. After the oil has steeped, strain it through cheesecloth into a small mixing bowl (a coffee filter in a metal strainer to prevent burning is practical). Stir in the grated beeswax until it melts. You may have to reheat your oil to melt the beeswax. Let your oil cool a little bit before adding the drops of oil/glyceride and stir gently to blend. Then pour it into a jar (the small half pint Mason jars are perfect).

Let cool until it thickens into a salve consistency.

13 Pain Relief

Beeswax can make an effective salve for aches and pains.
In a small saucepan simmer:

- 1 tablespoon chickweed powder
- 1 tablespoon wormwood powder
- 2 pints of sweet olive oil for 3 hours.

Strain, add 3 ounces of beeswax and 10 drops of tea tree oil and stir. Pour into individual tins.

14 Cooking

Beeswax helps with molding and locking in flavors. It is added to candies, such as Jelly Belly jelly beans and Haribo's gummy bears. It's also used to create the distinctive crunchy crust of the small French pastries called canelés, which are a real treat to make at home!

15 Unstick a Drawer

If you have an old, beautiful bureau, maybe you have problems getting those drawers to slide out smoothly. Apply a thin coat of beeswax to the wooden rails and they'll be opening and closing like new! The same technique will also work on sliding glass doors that no longer glide smoothly.

16 Sealing Envelopes

Want to make your party invitations stand out? Create a seal with beeswax and use the right stamp to leave your impression.

17 Chewing Gum [9]

Mix honey with beeswax in a 3:1 or 2:1 ratio in small dark glass container (30-50 ml). Leave no air between the upper surface and the lid. Store it in a refrigerator. For a long shelf life; add 1-3% propolis tincture or 1-3% soft propolis extract

18 Emollient Facial Cream: [10]

4 oz. Coconut Oil
5 ¾ oz. beeswax

In the top of a double boiler, melt the coconut oil and beeswax and stir. Once melted, remove from heat and pour into desired containers. Allow to cool and completely harden before use.

19 Furniture Polish: [11]

Melt 1 T. of grated beeswax in a small glass canning jar which is sitting in a pot of water over low heat. After the wax is melted, stir in 3 T. of coconut oil until melted. When this cools and hardens, use a clean cloth to rub it onto your wood furniture. Leave it there while you go wrap some Christmas presents or pet the cat. Then, using another cloth, buff the furniture until all residues are removed. Remember, this

---

[9] Dr. Edward F. Group III, DC, ND, DACBN, DCBCN, DABF
[10] http://www.hardlotion.com/make-your-own-moisturizer/
[11] http://learningandyearning.com/uses-for-beeswax

is for occasional use in protecting or restoring the wood, not for weekly dusting since the wax can build up on the furniture.

20 Beeswax Saddle Soap:[12]

Harness, saddle, and bridle leathers should be cleaned and conditioned at least twice a year to extend their usefulness. In fact, all types of leathers would last longer if they received this luxurious treatment.

2 tablespoons grated beeswax
1/2 cup olive oil
I cup grated Castile soap
1/4 teaspoon lavender or tea tree essential oils

Heat olive oil until warm and stir in grated beeswax until melted. Add grated Castile soap and stir until melted and well blended. Stir in essential oils. Pour into shallow plastic container or lidded tin. Cool before using. To apply, scoop up a small amount of saddle soap and rub onto leather in a circular motion, using a sponge or a piece of loofah. Rinse with a damp cotton cloth. Allow leather to dry completely before conditioning with Boot and Saddle Conditioner. Makes about 1 1/2 cups

---

[12] The Herb Companion Aug/Sept 1999

Chapter 4

APILARNIL

Drones are the large box-shaped male bee of the 3 casts in the hive. It is the drone larvae that are usually used for Apilarnil.

Nicolae Ilesiu is a Romanian who discovered Apilarnil and researched its effects.

API – *Apis*
LAR – Larva
N –Nicolae
IL – Ilesiu

The capped brood in the center of the picture to the right shows how the drone cell is a larger cell and is capped higher than the worker cell. The adjoining cell contains a drone hatching. Photo: Roland Prakel

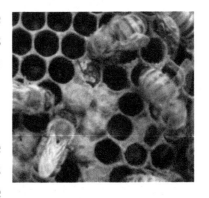

A study done on female and male chickens in Britain[13] indicated there were no effects on the growth performance of male or female chickens when fed Apilarnil; but did suppress blood glucose and cholesterol; showed lower level of fear at being caged; and stimulated early sexual maturation in males.

The life span of an adult worker bee varies with the time of the year. When the colony is active in spring and summer, worker bees may live as long as 5-6 weeks. During the inactive period in winter a worker bee can live 5 months or more. Queens can live from 1 – 5 years.

A drone lives for about 4-6 weeks in the summer or until fall when he is kicked out of the hive. His only job is mating with the queen.

For apitherapy, whether or not you are a beekeeper, you will need to know the age of the larvae from egg, to the time the cell is capped, to hatching.

---

[13] Br Poult Sci. 2013 June, 54(3):355-61. doi: 10.1080/00071668.2013.791382. Altan O[1], Yücel B, Açikgöz Z, Seremet C, Kösoğlu M, Turgan N, Ozgönül AM.

 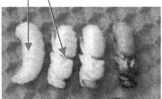

Age of drones to use for Apilarnil.

Fig. 1

Left Photo source: Winston M., 1987, The Biology of the Honey Bee. Harvard University Press, Cambridge, MA
Right photo: http://en.wikipedia.org/wiki/Western_honey_bee#mediaviewer/File:Drohnenpuppen_79d.jpg

The drones in the black and white picture of 3 rows of cells on the left are how the bees look at the designated day in the cell. The colored picture to the right (In Fig 1) shows the stages of the drones that are to be used in Apilarnil: Left to right: The first larva is on the 1st of day after capping or 10th day from egg. Day 11 or the 2nd day is the second bee in from the left in the picture. The third bee is the 3rd day of prepupa, when it starts to take on color. Use the 3rd day only if you have to. When the larva takes on color it signifies that the bee is using the properties you want to use in Apilarnil. The fourth bee is the beginning of the metamorphose state and you don't want to use it. You want the prepupa stage – just after capping and before the larvae starts changing when it adds color in the head as indicated in the picture of the third bee. So you have 2 days, 3 at the most to get your drones.

Drones are haploids, unfertilized male bees:[14] They are gathered only on the 10th[15] day after laying the egg, in other words, in the 7th day of their larvae stage. At this 7th day, the male bee:
- Has a weight of 250-300 mg, has the elements of its main organs, and all its body's programs are completed.
- One male larva contains over 10 million sperms.
- Reserves of nutritive material are at highest level at this age:
  o Fat
  o Body protein
  o Accumulation of lipids and carbohydrates, particularly glycogen, which plays an important role in the metabolic process.
- Has a significant amount of hemolymph, far richer in nutrients and energy compared to other insects or animals, including human blood:
  o 9 times more magnesium than human blood
  o Greater phosphorus

[14] http://healthywithhoney.com/bee-brood-apilarnil/
[15] http://www.icdapicultura.ro/en/apitherapy/beekeeping_products/5._apilarnil.html

o Carbohydrates are more from fructose, while in human blood it's more glucose

I find it interesting that the drone's chemical makeup is often compared to Royal Jelly (RJ). You will learn more about RJ further on in Chapter 5. It is only in the past few years that research has found other ways to use the drone and its larvae.

The presence of 10-hydroxy=2=decanoic acid authenticates Royal Jelly and apilarnil.[16]

Below is a chart of the chemical makeup of mature and immature honeybees as compared to beef and soybeans (in % of fresh weight; vitamins in International Units per g fresh weight) modified from Crane, 1990.[17]

	Honeybee			Beef	Soybean[d]
	Mature larvae	**Pupae**	**Adult[a]**		
Water	77.0	70.2	72.1	74.1	70.0
Ash	3.0	2.2		1.1	1.5
Protein	15.4	18.2	17.9	17.7[b]	12.9
Fat	3.7	2.4	2.8	2.8	5.9
Glycogen	0.4	0.8	1	0.1-0.7	2.4[c]
Vitamin A	107	51.3		0	
Vitamin D	6863	5165			
Chitin/fiber			4.1		1.7

NOTE: Danish scientist Hans Christian Gram devised a method to differentiate two types of bacteria based on the structural differences in their cell walls. In his test, bacteria that retain the crystal violet dye do so because of a thick layer of peptidoglycan and are called Gram-positive bacteria. In contrast, Gram-negative bacteria do not retain the violet dye and are colored red or pink. Compared with Gram-positive bacteria, Gram-negative bacteria are more resistant against antibodies because of their impenetrable cell wall.[18]

---

[16] http://www.usamvcluj.ro/en/files/teze/en/2013/barnutiu.pdf. Eng. Lavinia Ioana Bărnuţiu (Tomoş), Biological Properties Evaluation Of The Quality Markers From Royal Jelly And Apilarnil, University Of Agricultural Sciences And Veterinary Medicine Cluj-Napoca, 2013

[17] Value added products from Beekeeping, FOA Org.

[18] http://www.usamvcluj.ro/en/files/teze/en/2013/barnutiu.pdf

Apilarnil samples showed selective antibacterial activity against Gram-positive bacteria and almost none against Gram-negative bacteria.

According to a Russian study, bee brood allergy is at 2.4%.

The indications for Apilarnil are for just about any illness and anything wrong with the body for children, adults and elderly.

Until now adverse, toxic, or allergic reactions related to the use of apilarnil have not been reported. However, because it also contains small amounts of pollen, propolis, and honey, its use may be contraindicated.

Adverse reactions can be:

Digestive tract disorders such as stomach aches: vomiting or diarrhea may occur through overdose. Decreasing the dose, or stopping the apilarnil administration will eliminate these adverse reactions.

Toxicity may appear in major overdoses.

Hyperandrogenism (excessive levels of androgens) and hyperspermatogenesis (increased libido) may appear in some cases of overdose.

Moderate insomnia (especially in men), if administered late at night.

Contraindications

The body is too weak, unable to digest, and/or absorb it.

There are structural or genetic problems with internal organs as they cannot utilize the active compounds from apilarnil properly.

There are spasms, tumors, excessive mucous or parasites in the digestive tract, etc.

If it is used improperly.

Harvesting Drones

Harvest the drone and prepare it by:

- Using sterile gloves to harvest drones as you open the drone cells and pull out the larvae with a pair of tweezers.
- Either grind the larvae or place it in an electric grinder (trituration) that doesn't heat up.
- Put the soft preparation in the freezer for later use or place it in alcohol.
- This extract is like soft propolis extract and can be used as a base for preparations in:
  - 2% extract in honey.
  - 2% extract in honey and 20-30% bee pollen.
  - 2% extract in honey, 10-30% bee pollen, plant extracts, according to the disease to be treated.
  - 2-5% drone larvae extract in 10% alcohol of 10-12% plus herbal extracts.

If you have the means, you can lyophilize the drone. This is a freeze dried process that removes moisture from the cells of specimens while the specimens remain frozen.

Apilarnil extract from drone larvae also contains small amounts of royal jelly, bee bread, honey, and propolis.

If you plan to use a lot of drones you can purchase frames designed strictly for raising drones. You can place them in the hive with the understanding that there needs to be about 5% or less drones in a hive. If you continually take the drones out, you could compromise the hive.

Dosages

Adults – daily about 300 mg (.o1 oz.), 600-800 mg (.021-.028 oz.), if necessary.

Children – usually daily at about 30-50% of the adult dosage.

For mouth and gastro-intestinal issues, it is advisable to keep the raw, lyophilized, or tablet under the tongue until completely dissolved, min. 2-5 min. then swallowed.

Administration

Larvae deteriorate faster than royal jelly. So you need to prepare the larvae within 1-2 hours.

Mr. Lusale, a Zambian beekeeping extension officer, demonstrating an alternative way to use for bee brood. FOA – Value-added products from beekeeping.

Raw drone larvae comb can be eaten warm from the hive or placed in a glass container adding enough honey until the container is full. As the drones contain a lot of water, it is advisable to use very small plastic jars, max. 30 ml (1.01 oz.) then put in the freezer.

Apilarnil can be given at any age from infants to old people. It has a higher efficiency when combine with other nutritional supplement, such as royal jelly, honey, pollen, flax seed oil, or spirulina, by enhancing each other's properties.

Any time you use any beehive products, don't assume one dose or one product will do the job. And don't assume you can use the same amount for everyone. Each individual is different, with different body makeup, different body chemistry, different genetics, etc.

~

Recipes/Formulas

1. In Nepal, brood combs are placed in course-woven fabric and squeezed. The juice is collected and heated over a fire while stirring. The result is similar to scrambled eggs but with a richer flavor.[19]

---

[19]19 FOA – Value-added products from beekeeping.

2. Larvae can be boiled or rolled in flour and fried. Try cooking them for 15 minutes in ¼ cup butter. Add 6 garlic cloves and cook for a few minutes more then add 1 cup larvae.

3. You can use adult bees as well as larvae for stews.

4. Bee Flour can be made by dry roasting the bees or larvae in the oven at 100°C (212°F). Grind up the dried product and add to the flour. You can also add an equal amount of ground bee pollen. Supposedly, you won't know the difference in taste in bread, soups, etc.

   Add ¼ cup bee flour to 1 ¼ cups of regular flour to make pastry. You can add bee flour to cookie recipes as well.

5. Bee Mango Chutney[20]

   15 medium size, peeled chopped mangos
   8 medium size chopped papayas
   1-2 cups boiled bee larvae, chopped

   Mixed with:
   3 Tbsps of chopped, candied ginger
   ¾ cup chopped citron or other candied fruit
   ¼ cup chopped candied lemon peel or ½ cup chopped preserved kumquats

   Spice bag:
   2 cinnamon sticks
   30 whole cloves
   ¾ tsp coriander seeds

   Sweet vinegar:
   6 cups sugar
   4 cups cider vinegar

   Heat the sweet vinegar to boiling, add the other ingredients, including the spice bag and simmer for 5 minutes. Remove the spice bag and pour the boiling mixture into clean sterilized jars leaving 2 cm (1/4")

---

[20] FOA – Value-added products from beekeeping.

head space and seal with lids. Place jars in water bath and continue heating for another 15 minutes.

Use vinegar of at least 5-6% acetic acids. Other spices such as red peppers, turmeric, or curry may be added. When using other vegetables like tomatoes, apples, or onions, simmer them first for ½ hour in an equal amount of sweet vinegar.

6. When using larvae, you can also use wax moth larvae.

7. Royal Jelly Substitute:

In a blender that does not heat up, put in equal parts of drone larvae and bee bread and blend well. Put contents in honey to preserve it and place into the refrigerator. Take ½ - 1 tsp daily.

Chapter 5

Royal Jelly

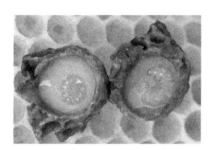

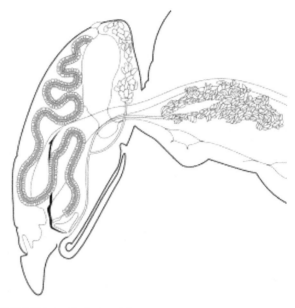

© Adam Tofilski - www.honeybee.drawwing.org

It takes bee pollen to make Royal Jelly (RJ). The picture in above left has an exposed queen cells. But there are a lot of things wrong with the picture. Can you see the errors? The picture is used on the internet a lot. First, the comb in the background of the pictures is never that yellow for brood. The 2 opened cells appear to be placed on new comb. Second, there should be RJ residue on the wax cell wall. Instead it looks like someone put the RJ in at a particular level. Third, by the sizes of the 2 larvae, you know they are different ages, and yet have almost the same amount of RJ. But it is a nice picture and someone did go through a lot of trouble.

RJ is creamy white in appearance and viscous. Its taste is specifically a bit sour and astringent. When they eat a lot of bee pollen, nurse bees between 4 to 12 days old create RJ from their hypopharyngeal gland as shown in the picture above right.

Even though the queen is the one laying the eggs, the workers are the ones who determine if the queen needs to lay workers or drone eggs. They will start the cell walls the width size needed for a worker or a wider cell for a drone.

The bottom of a honeycomb cell is called a ramboid. After a bee hatches, the workers will cover the ramboid and cell walls with a layer of wax and propolis. They do not clean out the bee waste or cocoons. When the cell has been prepared, they will place a small amount of RJ on the ramboid. During an inspection, if you turn a honeycomb to the light, you will see the shiny RJ on the bottom of the cell (ramboid).

The queen will stick her head into the cell and check its readiness for an egg. By placing her hind legs on the top of the cell walls, she can determine if she needs to lay a worker or a drone. After laying the egg, it will stay stand up on the ramboid while it is fed RJ until it is 3 days old. On the 4th day the egg will lie down, curl, and be fed honey and beebread until prepupa stage, at which time it will be capped. If the egg has been chosen to be a queen, it will be fed RJ until capped. All eggs are capped on the 8th or 9th day (if it has Africanized genes then it will be capped sooner), and becomes the first day of prepupa stage.

RJ will trigger the development of queen morphology, including the fully developed ovaries, and creates her distinctive pheromones that will identify the hive. After hatching, the queen is fed RJ for the rest of her life.

According to *The ABC and XYZ of Bee Culture* by A. I. Root:

> "The white creamy substance fed to very young worker larvae looks exactly like royal jelly and was long thought to be royal jelly. However, Townsend and Shuel (1970) found that this material cannot support continuing larval development as royal jelly does. Both are secreted by nurse worker bees as a combined product of their hypopharyngeal gland, the mandibular gland and the honey stomach. Both substances are made of varying proportions of sugar, lipids, protein, pantothenic acid, water, soluble substances, bioptrin and neoptrin. Royal jelly has high concentrations of all of these substances except protein which is higher in the worker jelly.
>
> "2 Days after grafting there will be 147 mg of RJ in a cell; after 3 days, 235mg; and 182 mg after 4 days."

Note the difference between the 3rd and 4th day. The 4th day, the egg has become a larvae and is taking nourishment.

From their own bodies the workers add amino acids, carbohydrates, fats, vitamins, minerals, etc. The antioxidant activity in RJ is due to the polyphenols, chemical compounds present in Royal Jelly and apilarnil compositions. Chemical composition of Royal Jelly is a mixture of vitamins and amino acids, and also unidentified compounds (2.8%). Literature shows some of the important components of Royal Jelly are proteins, sugars, and lipids.[21]

Royal jelly (RJ) is a honeybee product containing proteins, carbohydrates, fats, free amino acids, vitamins, and minerals. As its principal unsaturated fatty acid, RJ contains 10-hydroxy-2-decenoic acid (10-HDA), which may have antitumor and antibacterial activity and a capacity to stimulate collagen production.... The RJ contained about 0.211% 10-HDA. The UVB-irradiated human skin fibroblasts treated with RJ and 10-HDA had increased procollagen type I and TGF-β1 productions, but the level of MMP-1 was not changed. Thus RJ may potentially protect the skin from UVB-induced photo aging by enhancing collagen production.[22]

Followed by its saturated equivalent, 10-hydroxydecanoic acid, which is strongly antibacterial and has the activities similar to *Micrococcus pyrogens* one-quarter that of penicillin. It is also antiviral that can reduce the plasma levels of cholesterol and triglycerides. RJ is also antimicrobial in topical creams, as in wound healing.[23]

RJ has traces of Vitamin C, but Vitamins A, D, E, K are absent.[24]

RJ Can Be Used for:[25]

- Anorexia
- Anxiety
- Arteriosclerosis
- Arthritis
- Bone fractures
- Bronchial asthma
- Depression
- Dermatitis

---

[21] Takenaka, 1984; Pourtallier et al., 1990, Lerker et al, 2003, (University Of Agricultural Sciences And Veterinary Medicine Cluj-Napoca Biological Properties Evaluation Of The Quality Markers From Royal Jelly And Apilarnil (Summary of Phd Thesis, 2013.

[22] Royal jelly protects against ultraviolet B-induced photo aging in human skin fibroblasts via enhancing collagen production. Park HM[1], Hwang E, Lee KG, Han SM, Cho Y, Kim SY. J Med Food. 2011 Sep;14(9):899-906. doi: 10.1089/jmf.2010.1363. Epub 2011 Aug 3

[23] *The Hive and the Honey Bee*, Joe M. Graham, Editor. 1992. Dadant and Sons, Hamilton, IL

[24] Melampy and Jones, 1939

[25] Health and Healing with Bee Products, C. Leigh Broaedhurst, PhD

- Fatigue
- Lack of sexual desire in women
- Hair loss
- Impotence
- Liver disease
- Pancreatitis
- Insomnia
- Kidney disease
- Seborrhea
- Stomach ulcers
- Varicose veins
- Skin disorders
- Weakened immune system

In 1995 review of controlled human and animal studies concluded that, in humans, 50 to 100 mg of RJ (dry weight) per day decrease total serum cholesterol by 14%, and lipids by 10%. Most humans in the studies reviewed received RJ by injection, but injected doses were found to be only slightly more effective than oral doses. RJ supplements also slowed the development of blockage as hardening of the arteries in rabbits fed very high-fat diets.[26]

RJ's Side effects in major doses:[27]

- Eczema
- Rash
- Cough
- Light headedness
- Increased heart rate
- Stomach distress/nausea
- GI tract issues

Digestive tract disorders may occur through overdose, such as stomach aches, vomiting, and diarrhea. Insomnia (especially in women) may be an issue. Decreasing the dose or stopping the royal jelly administration will eliminate these adverse reactions. Toxicity may appear in major overdose cases.

---

[26] Health and Healing with Bee Products, C. Leigh Broaedhurst, PhD
[27] http://www.bee-pollen-buzz.com/side-effects-to-royal-jelly.html

NOTE: Royal jelly might increase the effects of warfarin (Coumadin). Taking royal jelly with warfarin (Coumadin) might result in an increased chance of bruising or bleeding.[28]

RJ will also lower blood pressure more if you already have low blood pressure.

Dosage: [29]

Adult daily usual dose is about 500 mg (800-1000 mg, if necessary).[30]

Children's doses are usually 30-50% of the adult dose.

8-100 mg Orally - improvement of general condition, increase in weight, appetite, red blood cells and hemoglobin.[31]

For mouth and gastro-intestinal uses, keep the raw, lyophilized or tablets of royal jelly under the tongue until they are completely dissolved, minimum 2-5 minutes.

Royal jelly, as its name implies, is a jelly which can be easily mixed with a lot of other natural remedies like in honey, propolis. bee pollen, apilarnil, beeswax, herbs, or essential oils.

You need to work fast with RJ as it deteriorates fast if kept at room temperature for over 4 hours and exposed to air. Everything should be in place before you take it out of your refrigerator.

From FOA – Value-Added Products from Beekeeping.

- Elderly 70-75 years, anorexic, depressed and low blood pressure patients: 20 mg taken orally every second day, improvements on all accounts.

- Chronic TB: mixture of RJ, honey, and ginseng improves weight gain and psychological conditions.

---

[28]http://www.webmd.com/vitamins-supplements/ingredientmono-503-royal%20jelly.aspx?activeingredientid=503&activeingredientname=royal%20jelly
[29] Dr. Stephan Stangaciu, www.apitherapy.com AIC
[30] According to Prof. Bengsch (1998), in one case of terminal viral meningitis, in Germany, it was administered in a so-called "attack dose", in two days 50,000 mg!!! The patient was healed in about 7 days.
[31] FOA – Value-added products from beekeeping.

- Stimulates metabolism: effect comparable to that of proteins, effect assumed to be due to activity of enzymatic complexes.
- Wound healing: 5-30mg/ml into burn blisters, improved regrowth of skin.

Below are some internal preparations you can make with fresh RJ:[32]

- From 1 cell without the queen larva (The queen larva can be frozen for further potential use in very severe cases, as in severe viral diseases.) add liquid honey, and crystallized honey. Fill a 30-50 ml jar in the order listed.

- 5% Fresh RJ, 55% liquid honey, 35% bee pollen, 3% soft propolis, and 2% essential oils.

- 5-10% Fresh RJ, 10-12% alcohol (80%), 10% wheat germ extract. This preparation can be inserted in vials.

Below are some types of creams which you can prepare locally[33].

Blend a cleansing soap, fresh RJ, vitamin E, plant extracts, and essential oils.

Cleansing lotion, add more RJ to the above formulation.

Skin tonic mix fresh RJ, gamma-linoleic acid-rich oil, vitamin E, menthol, essential oils, and rose flower extract. There should be no alcohol in the solution.

Moisturizer - mix fresh RJ, carrot oil, rosehip oil, gamma-linoleic acid-rich oils, allantoin, and beeswax.

Night cream - mix RJ in large amounts into essential oils, vitamin A, and Vitamin E.

Eye gel - mix fresh RJ, vitamin E, Aloe Vera.

Face mask - mix fresh RJ, vitamin E, essential oils, and plant extracts.

---

[32] Dr. Stephan Stangaciu, www.apitherapy.com AIC
[33] Irene Stein, 1989.

Harvesting RJ

I have a hard time with the idea of harvesting as there really isn't a good way to sustainably harvest your own RJ on a scale large enough to use it on a regular basis throughout the year.

You can purchase a Queen Castel that holds deep frames for putting in queen caps on 3 bars placed at intervals in the frame as in the picture above. You would graft 24-36 hour old eggs and the workers will raise the queens. You will need a lot of bee pollen. Photo: https://wadesbees.wordpress.com/category/queen-rearing

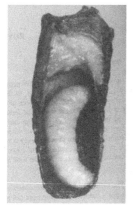

Photo: FOA *Value-added products from beekeeping,* bulletin 124

You can then wait until just as the queen is capped to remove the larvae. As you can see in the photo to the left the queen has very little RJ left just before pupation. You can also check on a daily basis from grafting to day 8 and get the RJ before it is capped.

Remove the queen and use a mouth vacuum or other apparatus to remove the RJ from the cell. I would also rinse the cell to get all the RJ. You can also freeze the cells for later use. The queen larvae can be used in apilarnil recipes.

To me this is valuable waste of resources. This is against nature and not what the bees would naturally do. In the apilarnil section there is a recipe where you can get nearly all the attributes of RJ by combing apilarnil with beebread.

N-Chromosome Royal Jelly

Hussein Yemen from West Minster, Canada, has developed a product called N-Chromosome Royal Jelly. He creates it by grafting drone eggs into plastic queen cups and letting the bees raise it like they would queens. I do not advocate this as it goes against everything natural. He claims it has cured 32 common diseases.

I flew to Vancouver to get the N-Chromosome RJ for my eyes, which had been diagnosed with Macular Degeneration. A year later my eyes were fine. But I was also told by a technician and affirmed by the doctor that just a very tiny sign, real or imagined, of eye diseases will get you the diagnosis. My eyesight did improve to not needing my glasses.

You can find more information on N-Chromosome Royal Jelly here:

- http://www.caspianapiaries.com/index.php/39-our-latest-products/82-n-chromosome-royal-jelly

- Hussein's 34-page PDF paper for Apimondia can be found here: http://www.apimondia.com/congresses/2013/Apitherapy/Plenary-Session/The%20Use%20of%20N-Chromosome%20Royal%20Jelly%20To%20Treat%20H.%20Pylori%20Ulcers%20-%20Hossein%20Yeganehrad.pdf

- And the Apitherapy News: http://apitherapy.blogspot.com/2012/11/apimedica-n-chromosome-royal-jelly-with.html

~

Recipes and Formulas

1. Royal Jelly Fudge[34]

    4 tablespoons royal jelly (or royal jelly and raw honey mix)
    4 tablespoons melted coconut oil
    3 tablespoons raw cacao powder
    2-3 tablespoons peanut or almond butter (optional)

    Combine all ingredients until well mixed. Pour the mixture into a small pan lined with waxed paper (bread pan works well) or evenly into an ice cube tray. Freeze until solid and cut into 12 even pieces - about one teaspoon of royal jelly complex in each 'dose'. Store it in the freezer to keep it solid.

---

[34] http://naturalfertilityandwellness.com/royal-jelly-benefits-fudge/

2. Using lyophilized RJ is preferable when adding to honey as fresh RJ will add to the moisture content of honey: 3% of RJ is equal to 2% of moisture. Moisture added to honey will ferment, which is why honey must be at 18% moisture or less.

3. Because of yogurts low pH, RJ can be added: 2 mg (1/2 tsp) of RJ to 125 g (4.4 oz) yogurt. RJ is added to yogurt after fermentation. Add the RJ to a small amount of yogurt, mix thoroughly then add and to the rest of the yogurt and stir.

4. You can mix RJ with honey, put it in your smoothies, mix with almond milk, etc.

5. RJ can be added to your moisturizers to tighten the skin.

Chapter 6

Bee Pollen/Beebread

There are basically 2 kinds of pollen: the wind-borne pollen, i.e. corn, wheat, oats, or barley that causes allergies. The second kind is the kind that is sticky because of its water content. The sticky pollen is what honeybees' harvest. Photo: Wikipedia

Pollen is on the male sexual organs called anthers of flowers in flowering perennial or annual plants, shrubs, and trees. The foraging bees gather pollen from the anthers, add their saliva, pack it into their pollen basket in their hind legs, and transport it back to the hive for various uses. Bees will also gather pollen while gathering nectar. When gathering nectar, the bee's body rubs

against the anthers. The honeybee's will collect the pollen on her hairy body then move to another nearby flower and rub against the anthers of that flower, thereby pollinating the flower. The bee will then use its front legs with cleaning hooks and clean herself of all the pollen on her body before packing it into her pollen basket. Photo: Wikipedia

What Do Bees Do With the Pollen?

I am always fascinated by the honeybee's anatomy. I can look at pictures all day and still be amazed at how hairy the bee is – right down to hair on the eyeballs.

When I was told that bees had a "nut cracker" on their knees to break pollen's hard outer shell called exine, I started putting the bees under the microscope. I show slides of honeybees to the kids when they tour my apiary and my very small lab.
Photo: Lady Spirit Moon

The photo to the right is what the "knee" part of the leg does with pollen that has been collected and is described as follows: [35]

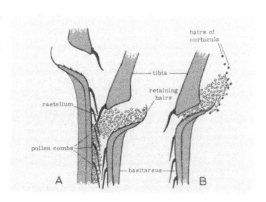

"Pollen packing: the diagram shows a section through the pollen press. A. press open, *rastellum* of right leg scraping pollen out of the pollen combs of the left leg; pollen falls on auricle. B. press closed, pollen forced through to outer side of right leg, where it is caught by the corbicula. The inner sides of the flat, broad basitarsi are covered with rows of closely set, stiff hairs, the *pollen brushes.* These are used for brushing pollen from the abdomen after visits to flowers. The forelegs are used in a similar manner to clean the head, and the pollen they collect is moistened with honey regurgitated from the crop; the pollen, rendered sticky by the honey, is then passed back to the hind legs and received on their pollen brushes, where it mixes with dry pollen taken by the hind legs. The combined harvest collects on the basitarsi.

"During flight the bee rubs her hind legs together, and the pollen is raked out of the pollen brushes by the rastellum of the opposite leg; this is a row of wide and pointed spines like the teeth of a hair comb, on the distal end of the tibia. From  the rastellum the pollen falls on the auricle, a sloping shelf on the end of the basitarsus; here it is retained by a fringe of hairs round the outer edge of the auricle. The tibio-tarsal joint, commonly called 'the pollen press' is then closed by flexing the tarsus, and the pollen on the auricle is squeezed by the opposing surface of the tibia. The rastellum, and probably also the teeth scattered on the auricle, prevent the pollen mass from escaping on the inner side of the joint, and it is forced to emerge on the outer side of the leg, where it is caught by the long, curved hairs of the corbicula, or pollen basket, on the tibia. The loads are then patted into compact masses by the middle legs."

---

[35] IBRA from Anatomy and Dissection of the Honeybee, H. A. Dade, 1977

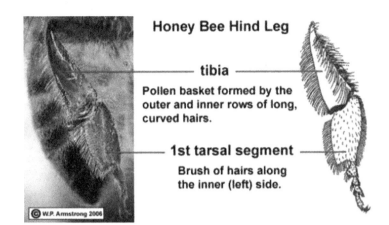

Honey Bee Hind Leg

tibia

Pollen basket formed by the outer and inner rows of long, curved hairs.

1st tarsal segment

Brush of hairs along the inner (left) side.

© W.P. Armstrong 2006

The photo to the left shows what the knee looks like on a real bee.

Photo: [36]

The pollen grain has two protective and durable coats around it. The outer waxy exine is made of sporopollen, which is able to resist most acids and temperatures as high as 300°C (572°F). Beneath this is the fragile inner wall, the intine, which surrounds and protects the nuclei and the reserves of starch and oil. Pollen, as vegetal masculine cells, has all necessary substances to sustain the life of future seeds and/or plants.

Pollen comes in a variety of color. William Kirk, in his book "A color guide to pollen loads of the honey bee"[37] finds over 563 colors for 268 plant species. All of these colors are subjected to change, in time, under certain factors:

- Nectar's mineral content is used by the bees to pack the pollen micro-grains with their tongue, hands, and feet in their flight from flower to flower. The richer the nectar in mineral salts, the darker the pollen
- More humid the pollen, the lighter the color.
- Longer the exposure to sunlight, the less color it has.
- Higher the fungi infestation, the darker the color.

Each pollen grain is the pollen's "finger print" and should have its own color. Under a microscope the pollen in honey will tell you from where the honey originated. If a certain grain is stained with another color, it may show different pollen grains stuck together because of excessive humidity, which also may be a factor in the presence of fungi, making the pollen dark.

If you know the origin of the pollen, you can use it for specific diseases; the same as you would the floral source in Herbology/Phytology. Multi-colored pollen is preferred for diseases. Commercially, good pollen should be at least

[36] Photo: http://www.wired.com/2011/06/honeybees-have-handy-knees/
[37] IBRA, 1994

2-5mm in diameter. In apitherapy, size is not a factor except in dried pollen. Too small a size exposes the pollen to higher oxidation processes under normal storage methods.

Sensory Sensations

The pollen must have a persistent floral fragrance, showing higher amounts of volatile components. You should discern the odor as you would perfume.

> **(Ed. Note:** To learn the art of a perfumist, fill a small vial with vinegar and slowly pass it under your nose and smell. Do not stick the vial under your nose and keep sniffing. One pass right to left is enough. The vinegar odor should be very strong. Take a moment to allow the odor to reach your brain and think about it. Rest a few minutes then cut the jar of vinegar in half with water and inhale again. Think. Rest a few minutes then cut the contents again half again with water and inhale and think. Cut the contents 14 times. If you can still smell the vinegar at the end of the 14th cutting, resting and thinking between the cuttings, you have a very sensitive olfactory.)

Taste sensations are determined by the gustatory papilla of the tongue in connection with smell.[38] Good pollen should have an intense taste.

There are four main taste sensations:

1. Acidity - detected by the anterior portion of the tongue. This is more pronounced in the pollens rich in Ericaceous (heather types) and Helianthemum species.
2. Sweet - detected by the point of the tongue. It will be rich in Citrus sp. (lemon, orange, grapefruit trees etc.)
3. Bitter - detected by the posterior portion of the tongue. It is specific to the Cruciferae (cabbage, mustard etc.)
4. Salty - determined by the middle posterior portion of the tongue. This sensation has no precise significance.

What Pollen Contains and What It Can Do

All pollen has amino acids, though will vary in quantity.

---

[38] Bonhevi, 1986

Dry pollen contains: 1.25 - 1.33% fatty acids based on dry weight of pollen. Major fatty acids are: linoleic, oleic, stearic.

The cozymase in mixed fresh pollen runs about 0.5-1.0 mg/gram, comparable to the amounts in yeast.

Pollen has all known enzymes & coenzymes and probably all that will be identified in the future studies.

Pollen contains all 28 minerals that are found in the body. 14 Of these are essential vital elements present in such small amounts they are called trace elements or micro-nutrients.

Water: 3-20% of fresh pollen by weight.

25% protein

Pollen is extremely rich in carotenes, which are metabolic precursors of Vitamin A. It is also high in B complex and vitamins C, E, and Lecithin.

It contains over 50% more protein than beef, yet its fat content is very low. It is also an excellent vegetarian source of protein typically possessing more of the essential amino acids, pound for pound, than animal proteins like meat, eggs, and dairy products.

Whatever constituents there are in flowers are also in the pollen, especially volatile oils. **A fact about plant oils** – they are called volatile oils while in the plants because the plants are susceptible to nature's elements and can be destroyed. Once captured, usually through steam instillation, the oils are called essential and contain nothing else.

Pollen phytonutrients determine the color and flavor of vegetables. They act as the plant's natural immune system, warding off disease and viruses. They help to increase your body's immunity and help to support the body's ability to remove toxins. These substances have also been linked to the prevention of cancer, heart disease, diabetes, and high blood pressure, etc. Pollen is uniformly rich in carotenoids, flavonoids, and phytosterols, beta-carotene, lycopene, beta sitosterol, quercetin, isorhamnetin, kaempferol, and rutin.

The acidity of pollen increases from 1.26 to 1.78% and in water-soluble proteins from 2.9 to 5.6%. A lactic acid-type metabolism occurs, indicating a lowering of oxygen tension....[39]

Fresh, unheated pollen also contains numerous active enzymes, coenzymes, and hormones, including growth hormones. Enzymes are needed for every biological process in the body. Eating enzyme-rich food saves the body from having to make enzymes, which depletes energy. Enzymes help the body prevent and fight diseases such as cancer and arthritis. The antioxidant enzyme superoxide dismutase (SOD) is found in pollen.

1/2 teaspoon of pollen is equal to a healthy serving of vegetables. (3 teaspoons = 1 Tablespoon / 2 Tablespoons = 1 ounce). Each ounce of honeybee pollen contains just 28 calories. Only 7 grams are carbohydrate, plus 15% Lecithin, the substance that burns away fat, and 25% pure protein.

35 Grams of pollen per day can satisfy human amino-acids requirements.

Royden Brown's *Bee Hive Product Bible* reads:

> "Horse trainers say bee pollen: strengthens arteries, veins, and capillaries to offer maximum protection against bursting...can help strengthen the reproductive system...especially formulated bee products administered several times a year make commercial deworming unnecessary...oxygenated blood resulting in a measurable increase in strength...bee pollen increases the red-blood-cell count by up to 30%...test showed that the swelling of limbs and joints common after a hard race can be markedly relieved by regular feeding of bee pollen...subject eating bee pollen recovered quickly after stressed performances...."

Contraindications

Possible side effects: headache, runny nose, sneezing, tearing eyes, fever, sweating, rash, itchy throat, and hay fever symptoms.

Many people may develop a fear against a possible allergy when they hear of bee pollen because of their fear of hay fever. Hay fever is not caused by pollen carried by bees but by the airborne pollen. This airborne pollen, also called by its Latin name anemophily, is produced mainly by ragweed and

---

[39] *The hive and Honeybee,* 1992

other types of grasses, trees, and plants visited by insects other than bees. Hay fever can be healed by ingesting bee pollen in very small amounts, in the beginning (even one-two grains), for 2-6 minutes under the tongue, then swallowed.

Allergies that may occur are due to bee saliva and nectar. There are respiratory allergies from inhaling unfiltered honey or commercial dried bee pollen package Alimentary allergies that have been administered directly, internally as a food or in medicinal preparations, or in mixtures with honey, royal jelly, herbs, etc. may also cause allergies.

Bee pollen has a relatively high content in carbohydrates so it's contraindicated for diabetics, depending on its plant origin. Acacia honey is best for diabetes.

Because pollen sometimes has very rough external micro-needles on its outer shell (exine), as is the case with dandelion, it is not advisable for people suffering from stomach disorders to consume it in large amounts, especially before meals. Pollen may also be an issue with someone who has gastro-duodenal ulcer or gastritis when it is administered raw in relatively large amounts before meals.

Bee pollen cannot heal a tissue, an organ, or a body that is much too weak to process it through digestion and absorption. Nor can pollen heal distant cells or tissues if vitamins, enzymes, etc. cannot reach the areas, like heart cells if they are blocked by an infarction.

Dr. Carlson Wade, in "About Pollen" states:

> "Bee pollen contains a gonadotrophic hormone similar to the pituitary hormone gonadotrophin, which functions as a sex gland stimulant. The healing rejuvenating and disease-fighting effects of this total nutrient are hard to believe, yet are fully documented. Aging, digestive upsets, prostrate diseases, sore throats, acne, fatigue, sexual problems, allergies, and a host of other problems have been successfully treated by the use of bee pollen."[40]

---

[40] *Wonderful World of Bee Pollen*, Joe M. Pzrkhill, Honeyologist

Administrations

Pollen is a nutritional supplement administered through the digestive system: mouth, esophagus, stomach, small intestine, large intestine, rectum, and anus.

Fresh bee pollen has higher amounts of vitamins, minerals, enzymes, etc. It is important to administer this pollen to people who are in danger of death or abnormal situations, like heart attacks, strokes, pre- and post-complicated surgery, meningitis, car accidents, etc. Pollen is easy as honey to digest.

In such situations give bee pollen in very, very small amounts, fresh, under the tongue for at least 2-4 minutes, before swallowing. In sublingual administration, only very small compounds from bee pollen will penetrate into the blood system and the large molecules like proteins, complex carbohydrates, or fats will not.

Dosage

1-6 teaspoons a day, according to the person's specifics age, body weight, and general nutritious health status. Small age and body weight requires less pollen, 1-2 teaspoons a day, administered several times as a meal, whereas poor nutrition requires more.

Fresh, non-polluted collected pollen have the highest qualities. Use specific pollen for different purposes: hawthorn pollen for heart problems and dandelion pollen for liver and kidney problems, etc. Do not use pollen from toxic or dangerous plants, such as foxglove (Digitalis purpurea or angustifolia) and Rhododendron species.

When you treat the whole body, it is better to use bee pollen from various botanical sources with different colors.

Take as much pollen as is necessary. An athlete, running a marathon or a Japanese Sumo wrestler, can consume up to 100g a day or more. There are reports of people who lived for 6 months with just bee pollen and water. A 6-month-old child will use only about a quarter of a teaspoon a day. You will know when you have had enough pollen when the appetite for pollen decreases.

Administration Methods

Internally by swallowing raw bee pollen or mixtures of pollen with honey or other foods like yogurt, cereals, bread etc.; under the tongue; through surgical or artificial feeding directly in the stomach or small intestine; through rectal suppositories; or through vaginal suppositories.

Pollen can be use externally in cosmetic masks, combined with honey and/or royal jelly, herbal or floral extracts, etc., and as nutrition for the skin.

If there are no allergic reactions, pollen should be administered on a daily basis. Some authors recommend administrations of 1 week per month, or 2 months in a row, then 3 months, pause etc. In my opinion the duration, like the other factors too - quantity, way of administration, etc. - needs to be individualized, from case to case.

Besides growth inhibitors pollen contains several so called growth regulators, like auxins, brassins, and gibberellins (a group of steroid derivatives that occur at very low concentrations in plant tissues and may have hormone-like effects and kinins (proteins in the blood that cause inflammation and affect blood pressure, especially low blood pressure)). These growth-related factors usually increase the appetite, sometimes too much. Some women are concerned about gaining weight, so they sometimes stop the pollen intake for some time, even if the apitherapist recommends continuing. What you can tell them is if they avoid foods with high caloric content like pork meat, fats, cheese, eggs, sugar etc., weight gain will not be a problem.

Some people may experience nausea which can be avoided by taking pollen in very small amounts, even grain by grain. In most cases, symptoms lessen or stop when you lessen the dose or stop taking pollen administration for 1 or 2 days. After a pause of several days, they can start with the same very small doses. People who complain pollen is difficult to digest can do the pollen allergy test of 1-2 grains the first day, 3-5 grains, the second day then:

Start with a mixture of honey and pollen at a 1:2 ratio for 1-2 weeks; take a quarter teaspoon in plenty of water, tea, or juice keeping the mixture in the mouth for a couple of seconds before swallowing. Drink the above mixture, in small portions, initially after the meals, then before meals, and finally between meals.

When Taking Pollen

- Always start with small amounts.
- **NOTE:** hot liquid and sun light destroy most of the bioflavonoids, enzymes, vitamins, etc.
- Use daily, collected fresh, if possible. If you harvest a lot of pollen, refrigerate the excess.
- Mold and bugs will grow if there is excess humidity/moisture, especially if the pollen is kept at room temperature.
- Refrigerate or freeze your pollen at or below 0°C (32°F).
- Store in plastic bags having little or no air. The absence of oxygen will usually prolong the pollen's life and qualities. Black plastic bags are best.
- Use different types of pollen.
- Be particular on special types of pollen for certain tissues, organs, or functions.
- Combining pollen with honey is an excellent carrier and will preserve pollen. Put pollen in a dark glass container and put in just enough honey to cover. The ratio is usually 1 part honey to 2 parts pollen.
- Keep raw or combined pollen under the tongue, before swallowing. Think about the taste.

You can prepare pollen by using it alone, powdered through a hand-cranked coffee grinder (do not use heat-generated blenders), in yogurt, honey, juices, on fruits and vegetables, breakfast cereals, or on toast with honey and butter. Use your imagination.

Since most commercial pollen comes from China, even if you have to call the company, check to be sure they test the pollen for contaminants or chemicals. A really good commercial bee pollen product will have on its label, the origin and type of the pollen, location of harvest, processing technique, storage advice, and expiration date.

~

Harvesting Pollen and Beebread

In the photo to the right is a front porch bee pollen trap. You can also purchase plastic pollen traps for a cheaper price.

Photo:http://www.brushymountainbeefarm.com/Front-Porch-Pollen-Trap/productinfo/509/

There is a caution when trapping for your own pollen. Don't leave the trap on for more than a couple days at a time per hive and don't trap more then 2-3 times a season, depending on how much the bees pollinate. You can determine this when you do your hive inspections.

You need to work daily on an hourly basis if you get enough, as pollen deteriorates rapidly. The longer you leave pollen in the trap the less enzymes, vitamins, and minerals you will have. Put the pollen into clean, dark containers, and freeze immediately; or put into honey according to the Beebread recipe.

To harvest beebread you need to use lab tools, a grafting tool, or a toothpick to pick out the beebread out of the cells of honeycomb. They will fall out like pellets if you're good enough. Otherwise, they will come out in pieces.

~

Recipes and Formulas

In formulas requiring bee pollen, crush the pollen in a mortar and pestle, or in a blender that does not heat up, until a powder and put the powder immediately into a liquid in the recipe. Let the mixture set for a few minutes for the pollen powder to absorb the liquid.

1. Honeybee Pollen Facial Mask

    ½ ripe avocado
    1 Tbsp honey
    ¼ cup of whole milk
    2 Tbsp bee pollen

Have all ingredients at room temperature and blend well in a blender. Apply the mask with fingers on a thoroughly clean face and throat. Leave on for 20 min. then rinse with warm water.

2. Cleopatra's Facial Balm

1 t honey
1 egg white
1 t milk
500 mg (not quite 2 Tbsps) bee pollen

Beat well and apply to clean face and neck. Leave on ½ hour until it feels dry and brittle. Wash it off with lukewarm water then splash on cold water. You will feel your face and neck tingle. Cleopatra used this formula on her entire body to keep her skin beautiful and soft.

3. Bee Bread tincture

Bee Bread is what the bees make and put into their cells. It is a combination of bee pollen and honey and has been fermented. The fermented process provides more nutrients.

1 part Bee Bread
2 parts ethanol alcohol (Good grade Vodka)

Put into a dark glass container and shake every day for 8 days. Drain through a fine cheese cloth. The liquid can be stored for a long time. The solid contents after straining can be put into water and drunk, or used in other recipes for immediate ingestion. Tinctures have a long shelf life.

NOTE: The alcohol can extract all substances related more or less to the fats (fat soluble vitamins, oils), and also colors (pigments) and resins.[41] Lower concentrations of alcohol extract the tannins, carbohydrates and the acid in the pollen more effectively.

Bee Pollen glyceride is made the same way as the tincture. It will extract most of the water soluble substances, leaving the proteins behind, thus

[41]R Krell, 1996 - Value-added products from beekeeping FAO Agricultural Services Bulletin No 124 Food and Agricultural Organisation of the United Nations Rome 1996. ISBN 92-5-103819-8

eliminating most, if not all allergenic material (Krell, 1996). This glyceride is excellent for cosmetics.

Oil extract of bee pollen has been reported as ineffective (Krell, 1996).

4. Making your own Bee Bread

This is not precise to commercial scale, but it will do for home brewing. In a dark container add:

1 part of bee pollen and a few bee bread pods from a hive frame.
Add enough honey to cover the bee pollen.

Looking at the glass, the honey on top will be about ½ the amount of pollen below it. In other words, fill the container ¾ with pollen and enough honey to cover the pollen and fill the container. Too much honey and the pollen will float to the top. You want enough honey to coat all the grains of pollen. Adding a few bee bread pods from a frame will speed the fermenting process as the bees have already added lactic acid. You will know when it is done by the appearance. In time, nearly all the bee pollen will have mixed with the honey. You will see some grains. The product will be thick like soft caramel.

5. Add to Rose hips for its high content in Vitamin C. Rose hips is known for containing the 3rd highest known source of Vitamin C.

6. Add to Blueberries for its indications in eyesight disorders. Unique compounds in blueberries appear to enhance capillary elasticity and eye permeability, resulting in improved vision in the dark.[42]

For 5 & 6: If you use a spice grinder that doesn't heat up, you can grind the grains and put them in 00 capsules alone or blend in a little rice powder to absorb moisture.. You can also add a little Vitamin C because pollen is low in it.

---

[42] http://www.naturalnews.com/047905_blueberries_antioxidants_eyesight.html#

7. Millet Puff Bars with Bee Pollen

    2 cups (500 ml) millet puffs
    2 Tbsps hazelnuts, freshly ground
    2 Tbsp bee pollen granules
    1 Tbsp flax seeds
    ½ cup (125 ml) raw honey
    2 Tbsp butter (or coconut oil or nut butters)
    1/2 tsp vanilla extract
    2 Tbsp sesame seeds

In a bowl, combine millet puffs, hazelnut, bee pollen, and flax seeds; set aside.

In a pot, put in honey and butter and heat until melted and combined. Remove from heat and stir in vanilla extract. Pour over millet puff mixture and mix thoroughly with a wooden spoon.

Place mixture in a 9" x 9" pan and use wet hands to press the surface until mixture is even. Sprinkle sesame seeds over top and press again. Let cool until solid. Cut into squares and serve. Makes 16 squares

Add fruit if you wish; you may need to adjust honey and millet accordingly.

Chapter 7

Honey and Honeydew

Although its main ingredient is natural sugar in a proportion of approximately 55% sucrose, 24% glucose, and 21% fructose, nectar is a brew of many chemicals. Nectar is a sugar-rich liquid produced by plants in glands called nectaries within the flowers. Floral nectaries are generally located at the base of the perianth, so pollinators are made to brush the flower's reproductive structures, the anthers and pistil, while accessing the nectar.

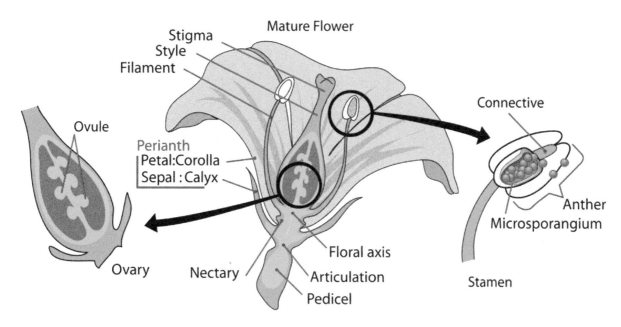

Photo: https://en.wikipedia.org/wiki/Nectar

Septal nectaries

These are nectar-producing tissue that is found in the wall of a plant ovary. Septal nectaries function as a way of attracting pollinators. Plants that rely on insects, birds, or bats for pollination often have septal nectaries. Aside from attracting pollinators, septal nectaries have also been known to attract "plant protectors." Some plants, like *Ruellia radicans*, have nectaries that continue to secrete pollen even after the petals have been shed. This attracts ants which will in turn protect the developing fruits of the plant from seed predators and herbivores in exchange for nectar.

See also: Myrmecophily (An organism, such as a beetle, that habitually lives in the nest of an ant colony.) and plant defenses against herbivory.

Extrafloral nectaries

Extrafloral nectaries (also known as extranuptial nectaries) are nectar-secreting plant glands that develop outside of the flowers and are not involved in pollination. They are highly diverse in form, location, size, and mechanism. They have been described in virtually all above-ground plant parts—including leaves (in which case they are known as foliar nectaries), petioles, stipules, cotyledons, fruits, and stems, among others. They range from single-celled trichome to complex cup-like structures that may or may not be vascularized.

Extrafloral nectaries on the petiole of a wild cherry (*Prunus avium*) leaf.

Extrafloral nectaries on a red stinkwood (*Prunus africana*) leaf.

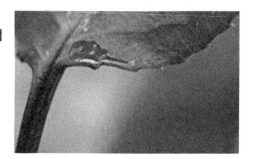

Ants on extrafloral nectaries in the lower surface of a young *Drynaria quercifolia* frond.
Photos: https://en.wikipedia.org/wiki/Nectar

In contrast to floral nectaries, nectar produced outside the flower generally has a defensive function. The nectar attracts predatory insects which will eat both the nectar and any plant-eating insects, functioning as 'bodyguards'. Foraging predatory insects show a preference for plants with extrafloral nectaries, particularly some species of ants and wasps, which have been observed to directly defend the plants. Among passion flowers, for example, extrafloral nectaries prevent herbivores by attracting ants and deterring two species of butterflies from laying eggs. In many carnivorous plants, extrafloral nectaries are also used to attract insect prey.

The bees gather the nectar with their proboscis (tongue). When back to the hive they pass off the honey to the house bee that then takes the nectar through her proboscis and puts the nectar in a honeycomb cell inside the hive.

To help dry the nectar, a bee takes the nectar out of each cell with her proboscis, adding her magic from her honey crop (stomach) before putting the nectar back into the cell. This is repeated until the water content in the nectar is below 18%. Flapping their wings also helps dry the nectar. When the 18% water content is reached, the bees cap off the nectar during the night. Once capped the nectar is then called honey.

INTERNAL ANATOMY OF A BEE

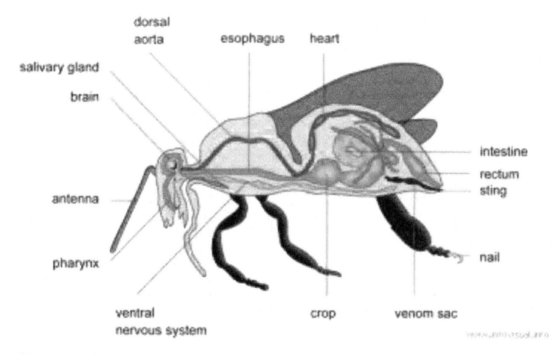

The diagram above is the internal organs of the honeybee. The crop is at the end of the esophagus and is where the nectar is held until the bee comes back to the hive. While in the crop the bee adds her magic to the nectar: hydrogen peroxide, lactic acid, enzymes, etc.

Things you should know

If you put a jar of honey up against a light and put your hand between the jar and the light, you should be able to see your hand. Honey should be clear, not cloudy. Bubbles may appear after the honey has been extracted, but they slowly go away. Honey will appear cloudy when crystalized.

Sometimes when you harvest different types of honey and put them in the jar, they will separate in the jar according to the glucose content. The higher the glucose content, the heavier it will be in the jar, on the bottom. The lighter honey will rise to the top. It usually takes a few months for the sugars to integrate.

Each honey has its own fragrance based on its quality of volatile oils. A fresh honey usually has a stronger fragrance than old honey. As in the pollen section, you pass the honey under your nose and think about it. Inhaling deeply too often will tire your olfactory. One important factor is to smell the honey at 20°C (68°F). The freshest honey has the strongest fragrance.

Honey will take on the fragrance of the source, if you have enough source. Sometimes the honey will also take on the source's color.

Because honey is hygroscopic, meaning it takes on water or moisture from the air, an open jar of honey will also draw the odors, like garlic in the refrigerator. So keep the lid on it. If it smells like it has fermented, moisture has gotten in and the honey has attracted natural yeasts from the air. Fermented honey can be added to lemonade or cider for a refreshing drink.

Bitter tasting honey is usually used for heart disease and a sour tasting is used for liver conditions. Check your herb book on which plants are used for such healing purposes and you will know how to use your honey if you smell the plant in the honey.

There are probably as many different honey flavors as there are plant nectar sources. There appears to be a basic "honey flavor" common to most honeys, since nearly every floral type seems to have some of this characteristic flavor, but the bee will bring the volatile oils from the plant. Maeda *et* al (1962) ascribed the taste of honey (in general) to the sugars, gluconic acid, and proline. Jacobs (1955) noted that nearly all phenylacetic esters are characterized by a honey taste and aroma.[43]

NOTE: There are only four main possible tastes for honey:

- Sweet is the fructose content, which is 2.5 times stronger than glucose and 1.5 times stronger than sucrose. That is why acacia honey which has a high content of fructose is considered a very sweet honey.
- Sour is the acids present honey, which may be from being over-smoked during its collection or while maturing.
- Bitter is due to quinine salts or caffeine; may be strong in chestnut honey from Erica species, Heathers.
- Astringent can be found in honeys similar to chestnut honey. I had honey from blueberry and blackberry patches that had the familiar astringent taste in the back of the throat.

Texture is detected by the mouth, lips, mouth mucosa, gums, and tongue. Through these sensations we can feel the "hardness" of a honey or its type of granulation.

Moisture content is related to the honey's water content, usually 18% depending on who you talk to. The picture to the left is a refractometer used to measure the moisture content in honey.

Viscosity depends on water content, types of carbohydrates, level of proteins, and especially temperature – the higher the temperature, the lower the viscosity.

Optical rotation (polarization): Like many other natural materials, honey has the property of rotating the plane of polarization of polarized light. This is due to the sugars, each of which has a specific and characteristic value for this property. It has long been known that natural honey is levorotatory (i.e. rotates the plane to the left). This is largely due to the excess of levulose (fructose) (so called, because it is levorotatory) over dextrose (dextro, or right rotatory) (glucose).[44]

---

[43] The Hive and the Honey Bee, 1992, p.885
[44] The Hive and the Honey Bee, 1992, p.894

Honey's hygroscopic ability draws out infections which is good for wound healing. Honey's density is the reason it does not allow air or bacteria to get back into the wound. Bees put Hydrochloric Acid in the honey, which fights infection.

Even though it's sensitive to heat, honey has thermal properties. With the wax it insulates the frames on the western side (setting sun) of the hive and protects the hive from getting too hot in the afternoon. The honey frames on the east side (rising sun) helps to insulate the hive from the cold. Ergo, honey frames on both sides of a Langstroth hive.

Honey has the ability to granulate. A supersaturated solution is one that contains more dissolved material than can normally remain in solution. These solutions are more or less unstable and in time will return to the stable saturated condition by crystalizing the excess solution.[45] Once heated it tends to granulate faster into rougher crystals.

Honey contains all the vitamins, minerals, and carbohydrates you need to survive for 6 months. Honey does not contain enough protein for your muscles.

The acidity in honey is caused by the organic acids usually existing in all honeys (tartaric, citric, oxalic, acetic and other acids), either from nectar or bees' secretions. This acidity that is measured by a pH meter is expressed in sodium hydroxide equivalents. The commercial high-quality honey should have acidity up to 4 ml - equivalents/100 g. The low pH also keeps bad bacteria from growing in the honey.

Honey's natural acidity may increase when it ages, when extracted from combs with propolis, and especially when it deteriorates due to fermentation. Honey adulterated with sugar syrup has a very low acidity while that adulterated with inverted sugar has a higher acidity. The acid intensity is measured and expressed by pH value, which can be used to determine one honey from another.

Diastase is an enzyme also known as amylase; it destroys starch, which is curious because honey does not contain starch. Because it is easily destroyed by heat, amylase has been a factor in measuring how much heat

---

[45] The Hive and the Honey Bee, 1992, p.897

honey can tolerate. Long storage can also destroy the amylase, along with other enzymes. 200 days at 30°C/86°F can destroy half, just as 1 day at 60°C/140°F, or 4.5 hours at 10°C/158°F.

The house bees add an enzyme from the honey crop called invertase every time they regurgitate their nectar. The nectar consists largely of sucrose, saccharase, or table sugar, and water. The invertase breaks the carbohydrate sucrose down into two simpler sugars: glucose (dextrose or blood sugar) and fructose (levulose or fruit sugar).

Honey also contains 14 sugars, one of which is called melezitose, which comes from broken down feces of other insects. Honeydew honey or fake honey has a high content of melezitose.

The mineral content is determined by weighing the ash resulted after calcination of honey at high temperature. Normal honey has no more than 0.6% ash, but may reach 1% in honeydew honey. The ash content is also significant in determining adulteration with sugar caused by adding sugar syrup to honey or by stimulating the bees by feeding sugar water, in which case ash cannot be traced, especially silicon.

When honey is overheated, fructose is partially turned into hydroxymethylfurfural (HMF) and is the main reason that high-fructose corn syrup is not good for bees. HMF is a chemical that forms when high-fructose corn syrup is heated. It is known to damage honey bees by causing ulceration of the gut. The same phenomenon may occur when honey is stored for a longer time at normal temperatures. Newly extracted honey which has not been heated has practically no HMF, lower than 4 mg/100 g. HMF content exceeds 10 mg/100 g only when honey is adulterated.[46]

Honey contains organic acids and some mineral salts, compounds which, chemically, are called ionisable (can be converted to ions) and have the property to conduct electrical current. This property can be measured very precisely and gives significant indications about the floral origin of honey. Honeydew honey has a very high thermal conductivity (over 10), while medicinal rosemary honey has less (1-2).[47]

---

[46] Pourtallier & Taliercio, 1971
[47] Pourtallier & Taliercio, 1971

Why Honey Heals

- Four main characteristics of honey are responsible for its antibacterial properties:[48]
  - Osmolarity – due to honey's supersaturated sugar solution, hence kills bacteria and fungi by drawing water from their cells. The water in bacterial cells seeks to come into equilibrium with the surrounding environment and thus the bacteria and fungi are killed by dehydration.
  - Acidity – Honey has a pH of 4, therefore acidic, which inhibits the growth of most bacteria.
  - Hydrogen peroxide production – The hydrogen peroxide producing capacity of honey, *not* its hydrogen peroxide content, is thought to be the main reasons for honey's antibacterial activity. Honey has the necessary components to produce miniscule amounts of H_2O_2 over a prolonged period of time, thereby making it an ideal substance to treat wounds and bacteria-caused disorders.
  - Floral Nectar Component – Some nectar will be more effective due to its floral content. Some nectar contains catalase, an enzyme that neutralizes hydrogen peroxide, lessening its effects. Some nectars contain yet unknown substances with antibacterial properties. And don't forget the flavonoids.

  Also the floral source will have other medicinal qualities due to the nature of the source: Lavender honey will calm you; mint honey has its own healing properties when ingested in the winter for colds, etc.

When Honey Is Needed

The bioflavonoids empower the autoimmune system; regenerate epitheliums, endotheliums, and cell membranes. Bioflavonoids also have anti-inflammatory properties and are good for all parts of the body including joints and sore throats.

Because it is hygroscopic, honey draws moisture from the air making it ideal as an emollient in lotions or a facial mask. This also helps regulate the large intestine flora by activating the pancreas and liver. It also blocks air, making it a good wound healer by blocking bacteria.

---

[48] *Honey, the Gourmet Medicine,* Joe Traynor

For wound healing: Honey is used to cure open wounds. Since 2002 the Wound Clinic in Valdese, NC, used honey on open sores and wounds that were so severe, amputation was considered. Applying honey to an open wound twice a week for several weeks, bandaging after each application, the wounds healed and the patients kept their feet, legs, or hands. When my grandson contracted poison ivy, I used honey on his open wound that had white spots on the edges, indicating infection is ready to set in. In less than 12 hours, the white spots were gone; the wound closed because of honey's tissue regenerating action of the enzymes, and was pink rather than red. It also took care of the poison ivy surrounding the wound.

Due to the acids in honey, you will find it in salad dressings and other products requiring a mild emulsifier. The acids also also allow essential oils to be mixed in honey.

Honey and propolis can act as an immunosuppressive agent so they may be useful in many immune system disorders, like multiple sclerosis, rheumatoid arthritis, lupus etc.[49]

The 30 to 45 minutes after you work out is called the anabolic phase, the time when your body goes to work to build muscle and recover. It's an ideal time to reload your system's energy supplies. Carbohydrates and protein are both useful for this purpose and even more effective when used together. Added to a protein shake and acting as the carb component, honey can help your body make the most of the anabolic window of muscle building and repair that starts when your workout ends.[50]

Manuka honey from New Zealand contains compounds against *Helicobacter pylori,* which is responsible for gastro-duodenal ulcers.[51] According to a nurse friend of mine, Manuka honey in bandages is now being used by hospitals and clinics in the USA with remarkable results. Presently, it is sterilized by gamma rays to kill any *Clostridium botulinum* spores and is the only honey accepted by the FDA.

Adding milk to honey for consumptive diseases has been around for centuries and is still used in Ayurveda.[52]

---

[49] http://www.ncbi.nlm.nih.gov/pubmed/9414144, Immunosuppressive effect of honey on the induction of allergen-specific humoral antibody response in mice. Duddukuri et al. 1997
[50] http://healthyliving.azcentral.com/honey-after-work-out-11511.html
[51] http://www.medscape.com/viewarticle/458834_5
[52] Curative Properties of Honey and Bee Venom, N. Yoirish

Honey is good in reducing fevers. A fever is an indication your body is fighting something. The antibacterial, antiviral, antifungal, and antimicrobial properties of honey may help.

Sour honey is good for anorexia.

A study conducted by the Archives of Pediatrics and Adolescent Medicine revealed that honey is effective in treating night-time coughing in children. The same type of coughing is associated with asthma.[53]

Honey is an emollient and stimulates bile production in the liver.

Honey drops in the eyes at bedtime have been used for cataracts. You can use a small food baster, take the basting needle off the one end, put honey in the other, and use 1-2 drops at night. Warning: it will sting for about 10 minutes. Some say to add saline to honey. I found that the saline solution stung more.

For some, it is said honey is good as a sedative at bedtime. It is a sugar and sugar keeps me awake. Diabetic readings often do not increase when taking honey at bedtime, as opposed to taking table sugar.

Research suggests that the polyphenol constituents of honey can quench biological reactive oxygen species and counter oxidative stress while restoring the cellular antioxidant defense system. Honey polyphenols are also directly involved in apoptotic activities while attenuating microglia-induced neuroinflammation.[54]

Honey is good for burns and scalds. Because of the heat of the burns, the honey will run and you will need to add honey often. But it does work.

It hydrates and tightens the skin when used as a facial mask/massage.

Honey is specifically adapted to the diseases, i.e.: linden honey for sleep disorders; eucalyptus honey for respiratory illnesses; Manuka (*Leptospermum scoparium*) honey for gastro-duodenal ulcers etc.

---

[53] http://www.livestrong.com/article/124197-honey-asthma/#sthash.eYNBuKPf.dpuf
[54] http://www.hindawi.com/journals/ecam/2014/958721/, Neurological Effects of Honey: Current and Future Prospects
Mohammad Mijanur Rahman,1 Siew Hua Gan,2 and Md. Ibrahim Khalil1, April, 2014

Facial cramps, tics, and twitches can be eliminated by taking 2 teaspoons of honey at each meal. Honey contains acetylcholine which acts as a chemical transmitter of nerve impulses.[55]

NOTE: Many plants of the *Ericaceae* family, *Rhododendron*, *Pieris*, *Agarista* and *Kalmia,* contain diterpene grayanotoxins. Consumption of honey made from grayanotoxin contained in leaves, flowers, or secondary products may result as intoxication specifically characterized by dizziness, hypotension and atrial-ventricular block.[56]

Contraindications

Diabetes is the most important counterindicate. Honey contains over 70% carbohydrates and it cannot be given in large amounts to people with hyperglycemia because of its excessive glucose (dextrose), over 120-mg/100 ml of blood. Honey with less dextrose and more fructose (levulose), such as acacia honey, will be better accepted by diabetic people. The exception is honey containing mainly fructose, which can be given in small amounts in the mornings; and using honey as an external dressing in slow healing wounds in diabetics.

Dr. Pavlina Potschinkova, Bulgarian apitherapy expert, writes in her book "Bee Products Used In Medicine," honey can be given to diabetic people up to 20-30 g (about 1Tbsp) a day, but under medical supervision. In Dr. Stangaciu's opinion, in order to be on the safe side of apitherapy, 8-9 grams a day (about 1 tsp), before or during breakfast would be OK, especially if well diluted in herbal tea or water or sour juices, like lemon or grapefruit juices.

People with allergies may not be able to eat honey because of its very low pollen content (up to 1%), which can start digestive or even respiratory allergies. You lessen the risk when you start any honey apitherapy treatment or use with very small doses well mixed in plenty of liquids.

Clostridium botulinum may be present in honey in a "dormant" state. The digestive system of infants to 2 years old may not have matured enough to handle the bacteria. Wound botulism is caused by toxin produced from a

---

[55] *Honey the Gourme Medicine,* Joe Traynor
[56] http://www.ncbi.nlm.nih.gov/pmc/articles/PMC3404272/, Grayanotoxic Poisoning: 'Mad Honey Disease' and Beyond, Suze A. Jansen,[1] Iris Kleerekooper,[1] Zonne L. M. Hofman,[1] Isabelle F. P. M. Kappen,[1] Anna Stary-Weinzinger,[2] and Marcel A. G. van der Heyden[1], Sept 2012

wound infected with *Clostridium botulinum*. Infant botulism is caused by consuming the spores of the botulinum bacteria, which then grow in the intestines and release toxin.[57]

At one time it was suspected that Botulism, a deadly group of bacteria, came from honey imported from other countries. Today Roundup is sprayed on nearly everything by nearly everyone except those who grow organically. Roundup contains glyphosate – glyphosate kills the *Lactobacillus* in the soil – *Lactobacillus* is required by every living element/entity in the world, including the soil. In the soil this bacteria keeps botulism in check. When not checked in the soil botulism travels up through the plant and into the nectar. Glyphosate has been proven through studies to kill, maim, and/or otherwise harm animals.[58]

E. coli and Salmonella markers have been detected as being glyphosate tolerant. This means that Roundup is allowing these 2 types of bacterium from the *botulinum* group to come up through GMO plants, and others, being sprayed with Roundup.[59]

So, it is important to know your beekeeper and whether or not they grow organically or keep their hives in the woods, or at the very least, have a lab check out the honey.

Do not use honey when the body is too weak to digest and/or absorb it, when there are obstacles like spasms, tumors, too much mucus in the digestive or respiratory tract, excessive parasites in the gut, vaginal spasms, scars, or flat large skin tumors.

Administrations

Used as a nutrient, honey is usually administered by mouth (Latin "per os").

Do not heat honey by mixing it with any other hot food, liquid or solid like hot tea, hot milk, cakes, etc. as most of the enzymes in honey will be affected. In open vessels like tea, the volatile oils will escape in the steam or be destroyed. When making tea folks usually have a plate over the cup to keep the steam from escaping. Most folks don't realize that the fragrance

---

[57] http://www.cdc.gov/nczved/divisions/dfbmd/diseases/botulism/
[58] Glyphosate suppresses the antagonistic effect of Enterococcus spp. on Clostridium botulinum. Krüger M[1], Shehata AA, Schrödl W, Rodloff A., Feb. 2013
[59] Health Effects of Marker Genes in Genetically Engineered Food Plants, Sirpa Kärenlampi. The book is online

they smell are from a teacup is the volatile oils from the tea botanical. These oils are most often the healing properties in the botanical.

If ingesting only raw honey, keep it as long as possible under the tongue before swallowing. Honey is not metabolized through the liver, so a lower dose can be used. The oral mucosa has a thin epithelium and rich vascularity, which favors absorption; however, contact is usually too brief for substantial absorption. A drug placed between the gums and cheek (buccal administration) or under the tongue (sublingual administration) is retained longer, enhancing absorption.[60]

Taste buds communicate quality and quantity to the nervous system which will transport into the stomach and later into the intestines.

Eating small amounts of honey several times a day, is better than eating large amounts infrequently.

Per os (by mouth): If in or near the mouth, *do* *not* dilute your medicinal honey. Just apply it locally and wait until it is normally diluted by the saliva. If for the stomach, start at the beginning, for a few days, with diluted honey (1:5 with tea or lukewarm water), then increase the honey's concentration (1:4; 1:3; 1:2; 1:1; 2:1; 3:1; 4: 1; 5:1). If the patient has had no adverse reactions then tell them to swallow it undiluted.

If for small intestines: Dilute honey in liquids like lukewarm water or herbal tea and administer as often as possible, in small amounts, but several times a day, even 20 times a day; no more than 60-100 grams a day.

You can use honey-based suppositories for the large intestines. See the chapter on Beeswax to learn how to make your own suppositories.

For the blood stream and other parts of the body that are very distant from the mouth, advice the patient to keep the honey for as long as possible under the tongue then swallow enough liquid to dilute. The finest part of the honey will penetrate directly in the blood stream and the rest of it, being well diluted, will be easily absorbed through the stomach and small intestine walls.

---

[60] http://www.merckmanuals.com/professional/clinical-pharmacology/pharmacokinetics/drug-absorption

For nose, ears, and sinus diseases (infections, inflammations, allergies): you need to first clean the nose with salty lukewarm water or herbal tea. Insert small amounts of liquid honey in each nostril while lying down on the back, face up. Wait until you taste the honey in your throat. The initial feeling is unpleasant (burning, astringent) but will last only a few minutes. Repeat if necessary after a few hours, between meals.

Skin: For topical use, the skin should be cleansed with soap and water if it is intact so that the honey can penetrate through the subcutaneous tissues. Before using cosmetics, honey can be used in special cleansing masks, specific to the client's type of skin and/or condition.

Eyes: dilute 1-2 g of raw, organic honey in 100 g of distilled water. Clean the eyes with a herbal tea, perhaps chamomile. Insert one drop from the above honey solution between the inferior eyelid and the eyeball. If it stings, it will last only a few minutes. This will also help with Glaucoma.

Female genital area: Use honey alone or combined with herbal tea in vaginal washings/douches.

Good for burns. You may have to apply often because the heat from the burn will melt the honey and the honey will run off.

A healing wound shows signs of regeneration at its bottom. To increase the regeneration phenomenon, a good blood flow in the area is required in order to have enough nutrients and oxygen to the healthy cells in the bottom and at the edges of the wound.

Prof. Descottes considers honey that is used for surgical purposes should be stored in small sterile pots, 50 ml/1.7 oz. each at room temperature and protected from heat and sunlight. The best type of honey for such goals seems to be thyme honey combined in special amounts with natural thyme oil.

Honeydew Honey

Honeydew honey does not come from nectar. Aphids and shield bugs pierce the plants so the sap will flow.

The ants suck up the feces (poop). The back to the hive and The poop contains sugar that identifies nectar honey and why it is called fake take the sap when

sap and release their bees take the poop create honey with it. melezitose. It is this the difference between honeydew honey and honey. The bees also available.

Honeydew generally shows dextrorotation[61] degrees, due in part to differing dextrose and levulose content. Honeydew is more dextrorotatory due to the presence of the characteristic sugars of melezitose and erlose's, density, and specific gravity: The Hive and the Honey Bee, 1992, p.895:

> "The density of a substance is its weight per unit volume; specific gravity (also termed relative density) is the ratio of the weight of a volume of a substance to the weight of the same volume of water, at specified temperatures…. The variation of density with moisture content is sufficiently high so that a low-moisture honey will tend to layer under a higher-moisture honey unless special care is taken to mix them. Honey exposed to moist air will absorb water and form a dilute layer which remains on the surface for a long time due to its lower density."

---

[61] Turning to the right, as the rotation to the right of the plane of polarization of light in certain crystals and the like. http://dictionary.reference.com/browse/dextrorotation

The general characteristics of honeydew honey are very similar to those of floral honey with some differences. Honeydew honey has larger amounts of minerals than nectar related honey, so:

- Its color is usually darker (exception: yellow larch honeydew)
- Its electric conductivity is higher
- It crystallizes easier and faster
- Its opalescence is more intense
- Has a stronger aroma and is inferior in taste to floral honeys.

What Honeydew Honey Has

Perhaps up to 1% Ash, whereas nectar honey has no more than 0.6%

Honey's pH is 5.9 – 7.8

Honeydew honey has more minerals and more essential oils, giving it a stronger aroma than the other types of honeys and the carbohydrates types are different. Honeydew honey seems to be a strong favorite in Germany.

Honeydew honey properties are pretty similar to those of floral honey. However, because of its higher composition in minerals and bioflavonoids, the following honeydew honey properties are normally more pronounced:

- Anti-inflammatory
- Anti-oxidant
- Stimulates the regeneration of epitheliums, endotheliums, and cell membranes
- Depurative
- Immunostimulative
- Laxative

Uses for Honeydew Honey

Because of the differences in composition between floral and honeydew honey, honeydew honey is usually better in the following conditions:

- Infectious diseases
- Immune system diseases
- Bacterial related diseases

- Viral diseases
- Large intestine diseases
- Diseases related to the presence of various toxins in the body
- Skin diseases
- Degenerative diseases
- Inflammation related diseases

~

Harvesting Honey

There are commercial extractors that are electrical or hand cranked. I prefer the poor man's method of crushing the wax in a large double tub with a drain. A 5-gallon bucket is placed below the tap on the bottom tub. On top of

the 5-gallon bucket is a double sieve with a straining cloth, a sheer curtain fabric, placed between the two strainers. The top strainer stops the large pieces and the cloth strains that which passes through the large

screen. You still get your fine pollen in the honey. Left photo: www.the-honey-hole.com; right photo: http://rurification.blogspot.com/2013/04/deadout-honey-harvest.html

~

Recipes & Formulas

The following is taken from *The Honey Prescription*, Nathaniel Altman.

1 Herpes - Add 3 tsp of honey to 1 tsp of cod liver oil. Mix thoroughly and apply to the affected area as often as needed.

2 Heart tonic - 1 tsp to 1 Tbsp of honey as a heart tonic; or combine cinnamon and honey on toast. Combining honey with herbs will multiply the herb's potency as much as 4 times.

3 To facilitate healing of gastritis and stomach ulcers, take one – 2 tsps of UMF-10+ Manuka honey 3-4 times per day. 15-20 minutes before meals.

4 Bronchitis and Whooping Cough – For relief of cough and wheezing, mix 1 tsp of finely chopped Thyme with 1 Tbsp of honey. Take as needed.

5 Cough – Add 1 Tbsp fresh lemon juice to ¼ cup of raw honey. Take a tsp of the mixture every 2-3 hours.

6 for Wounds – Take 10 parts (by weight) of beeswax and add 3 parts of propolis extract (10% ethanol recipe) and 2 parts raw honey. Melt the wax and cool it. While it is cooling, add the propolis and the honey. Mix well then place the mixture in a jar and store in a cool, dry place. You can apply the paste to treat many types of skin wounds, infections, burns, and sores. You can also chew the paste to help relieve mouth and gum infections.

7 My recipe for the face – I wash my face with warm water and soap and rinse thoroughly, leaving a little water on the skin. Using my finger I smear raw honey on my face and throat. Wait about 5 minutes. Using 4 fingers and patting my face repeatedly with aggressive up and down motions, I gently pat (slap) my face wherever there is honey, for about 5 minutes or until I can't take the pulling anymore. The honey will get stickier the longer you do it. Rinse with warm water and pat dry.

What it does is bring the blood to the surface and detoxes it, exfoliates dead skin cells, and nourishes your skin. If you wish you can apply a moisturizer afterwards.

8 Eat honey and lose weight[62] – The scientific reason for losing weight by eating honey and bee pollen: When you eat honey or bee pollen it goes into the bloodstream, causes rapid combustion and consumes fats which speed up the burning of fat, and continues through the bloodstream at a trickle and stimulates the heart without harmful aftereffects.

---

[62] *Wonderful World of Bee Pollen*, Joe M. Parkhill, Honeyologist

9 Using honey in your baking instead of sugar will help to maintain moisture and stay fresher.

10 Bee pollen and honey are natural laxatives and two of the fastest working stimulants known.

11 Two Tbsps of honey added to your favorite cake will make the cake tender and less crumbly. For best results, add the honey in a fine stream to the batter as you beat.

12 Add 1 Tbsp of honey and bee pollen to vegetables to bring out their true flavor.

13 When making homemade whipping cream, sweeten it with just a little honey. It will stay firm much longer without separating.

14 Combined with herbs will multiply the herbs potency by as much as 4 times. Use powders and blend well: Hawthorn Berry Pdr. for heart, Buckthorn Bark as a laxative, Ginseng roots for chronic fatigue syndrome, etc.

15 Combined with essential oils 3-10 drops to 50 g (1.7 oz) of honey: Fennel oil for coughs; with Thyme oil for post-surgical wounds, etc.

16 Honey Soaps: 3% honey; Honey Shampoo: 5% honey and 2.5% fragrance; Honey Cleansing Milk: 3.5% honey, 4.5% sweet almond oil, 4.5% soy bean oil, and 1.5% pollen extract; Honey Bath Foam for children and sensitive skins: 8% honey, 2% propolis extract, and 2% collagen polypeptide; Honey Hand Cream: 4% honey, 6% glycerol, 0.5% allantoin, and 5% soy oil.

Chapter 8

Propolis

Origin: early 17th century: via Latin from Greek *propolis* 'suburb,' also 'bee glue,' from *pro* 'before' and *polis* 'city.' Greeks pronounced it as präp ə ləs, meaning to hold up the city. Later version in Latin pronounces it prō polis, meaning to protect the city, which is what propolis does.

The honeybees use propolis to make a glue-like substance for their hives to seal cracks, holes, blend with wax to cap brood cells, and to seal out light. It is never used it to cap honey. Propolis is the one defense the bees use to protect themselves.

When propolis is slowly warmed in a (double boiler) it splits into two distinct parts: a viscous part that sinks; and a liquid wax that floats on the water surface and contains somewhere between 7.5 to 35% wax. Impurity content varies between 18 to 34%.

Photo: Lady Spirit Moon: The photo on the left is propolis granules taken from the inner cover of a beehive. The photo on the right is the same propolis that has been frozen then ground to a powder in my spice grinder.

About Propolis

Propolis varies in structure and consistency according to the temperature:

The bees use their mandibles to bite off pieces of propolis off the buds that secrete it and

pass it to one of their forelegs. The hind leg on the same side is thrust forwards, while the middle leg presses the propolis into the corbicula. After the bee returns to the hive, a house bee takes the propolis. Not all bees are propolis collectors.

Colors can range from various shades of yellow to brown, depending on its sources. (photo http://www.greenmedinfo.com/blog/7-health-benefits-bee-propolis)

Propolis from Brazil can be green, red, or brown.

Green or Alecrim propolis, originates from *Baccharis dracunculifolia.* Baccharis dracunculifolia is a medical plant found in Brazil, Bolivia, Argentina, and Uruguay. Baccharis dracunculifolia is used for its antiulcer and anti-inflammatory properties.[63] Photo of green propolis: http://www.apiarioslambertucci.com.br/blog/category/saude-e-beleza/page/2/

Red colored propolis is reported to be typical for Cuba, where its plant source was identified as *Clusia nemorosa* (Clusiaceae), and for Venezuela, where bees collect it from *Clusia scrobiculata*. In this study, they report their results on antibacterial and antioxidant activity of chemical constituents of red Brazilian propolis. Photo of red propolis in bee basket: http://www.buzzingacrossamerica.com/2015/12/propolis-glue-of-hive.html

European propolis usually has a pleasant and sweetish smell of poplar buds, wax, honey and vanilla; and when burned, it has a delicate aroma. Propolis can smell like cinnamon or other spices. Some propolis from Africa harvested from cocoa trees smell like and faintly taste like chocolate.

Propolis can sometimes taste sour and sometimes bitter. The flavonoids from propolis have a bitter and astringent taste.

---

[63] Wikipedia

Propolis is:

- Hard and brittle at 0-15°C/59°F (especially when it ages)
- Soft and malleable at around 30°C/86°F
- Sticky between 30 to 60°C/86 - 140°F
- Liquifies at temperatures higher than 60-70°C (86-158°F)

The melting temperature is from 65°-82°C (149°F-179°F). Some samples can have a melting point of over 100°C (212°F).

Propolis contains over 300 different constituents composed of flavonoids and phenolic acids or their esters, which form up to 50% of all ingredients.

Propolis is insoluble in cold water, but partially soluble in:

- warm or boiling water
- ethanol alcohol
- acetone
- ammoniac
- benzene
- chloroform
- ether
- trichloroethylene

  Propolis can be entirely diluted only by an adequate mixture of solvents.

pH Ranges between 5.2-5.7 (Bracho et al., 1998)

Antibacterial activity: The ethanol extract of propolis solutions (EEP) is maintained in acidic or neutral pH.

Propolis Properties and What It Can Do

Besides being anti-microbial, anti-bacterial, anti-fungal, and anti-viral, propolis has:[64]

- Glue-like property, useful in wound healing. Tincture will leave a resinous layer on the skin, but can be washed off.

---

[64] Dr. Stefan Stangaciu apitherapy internet course, www.apitherapy.com

- Can create allergies in 3% of the people who come in contact with some substances contained in propolis, especially prenyl caffeate.[65]

- Anti-*acid resistant* micro-organisms. Propolis has specific and non-specific (general) antibacterial properties.

- Anti-allergy - It also has general (non-specific) anti-allergic effects through its histaminopexic activity caused by quercetine.

- Anti-depression, sadness, melancholy - The energizing effect is related to the spicy taste of propolis, according to the Traditional Chinese Medicine.

- Anti-herpetic - Propolis is well known as one of the few natural products against different viruses. Herpes virus has been studied more than other viruses.

- Anti-mycotic - Fungus is also related to humidity. Propolis is one of the strongest anti-*Candida* natural products.

- Anti-edema - Propolis lessens capillary permeability and has a general dryness effect.

- Anti-proteolysis - Propolis helps protein production and protects the body's organs, tissues and cell structures, making it extremely important in the fight against tumors because cancer cells and tissues can grow only through proteolysis of the surrounding structures.

  Proteolysis is the breakdown of proteins into smaller polypeptides or amino acids. Unanalyzed, the hydrolysis of peptide bonds is extremely slow, taking hundreds of years. Proteolysis is typically catalyzed by cellular enzymes called proteases, but may also occur by intra-molecular digestion.

- Anti-*Trichomonas* (*vaginalis, gallinae* – poultry mite, *microti* - babesia) - Propolis is anti-parasitic.

---

[65] Prenyl caffeate, Biochemical formula:*[prop-2-enoic acid, 3(3,4-dihydroxyphenyl)-, 3-methylbut-2-enyl ester] [1,1-dimethylallyl caffeic acid ester]* [65], According to Hausen *et al.*, 1987; Wollenweber *et al.*, 1987; Greenaway *et al.*, 1988; Hashimoto *et al.*, 1988 prenyl caffeate is a potential contact allergen

- Anti-tumor (Tumor cytotoxicity or inhibition) - Propolis stimulates the immune system; is anti-proteolytic; protects the body's structure

- Astringent - Mainly in external use. Propolis dries.

- Cicatrization (process of wound healing) and regeneration of epitheliums and endotheliums - The body's skin is similar to tree bark.

- Decreases high cholesterol level in the blood - Propolis is light, fat is heavy. Propolis helps the bile liver secretion which has general anti-fat properties.

- Decreases glaucoma - Propolis has anti-spastic, anti-humidity, anti-congestive effects which are related to glaucoma.

- Decreases capillary permeability by increasing their strength: The capillaries are made from several cells. With its "glue-like" properties, propolis strengthens the cellular membranes.

- Helps the body's general detoxification mechanisms: liver, gall bladder, lungs, kidney, large intestine, skin, and endotheliums stimulation.

- Lessens gastric secretion by increasing the histaminopexic (block histamine) activity - Propolis is also excellent against *Helicobacter pylori* (stomach ulcers), which causes higher stomach acidity.

- Lessens the side-effects of chemo- and radio-therapy - Through direct protection against these factors and also through its detoxification property.

- Immunomodulatory action - Propolis intelligently helps the immune system. If it system is too excited, propolis calms it down. If it's too weak, it stimulates it.

- Increases body's resistance to infectious diseases - Direct effect as antibiotic and indirect effect as immunostimulator.

- Nutritional - Because of its mineral and bioflavonoid contents.

- Protects pulmonary system the most.

- Promotes building collagen and elastin - Extremely important in many diseases, but mainly in external and internal micro and macro-wounds.

- Protects the body against radiations

- Protects against the negative bee venom effects - Propolis has many effects which are opposite to bee venom

- Stimulates mammalian tissue regeneration. Stimulates mitosis and enhances protein biosynthesis
  o Mitosis is related to cellular multiplication.
  o Protein biosynthesis is necessary in any cellular or tissue regeneration processes

- Stimulates cellular respiration - The living cells also have their "lungs" called mitochondria.

- Stimulates the cytocidal (killing cells) action of lymphocytes - Inhibiting the growth of tumor cells, diminishing the side-effects of chemo- and radio-therapy.

When to Use Propolis

Propolis is the most medicinal of all the beehive products. Below are just a few of the conditions for which you can use it:

- Mouth-dentistry
- Otorhinolaryngology
- Ophthalmology
- Infectious diseases
- Pulmonary diseases (pneumology)
- Digestive diseases
- Gynecology
- Skin (dermatology)
- Radiology & radiotherapy
- Oncology

Contraindications

Propolis is NOT recommended for the 1-2% of people allergic to certain substances present in propolis, like prenyl caffeate. Some negative reactions that can possibly occur are:

- Contact dermatitis to propolis - raw or cream, ointment propolis.
- Allergy to propolis inhalations with bronchial spasms
- Oral mucositis with ulceration - propolis tablets, chewable propolis.
- Occupational eczema for beekeepers - raw propolis

For low blood pressure, propolis is spasmolytic and it may decrease the blood pressure. It is suggested you test for allergy by using only one drop of propolis tincture diluted in a soupspoon full of tea or water; chew less than 10-50 mg. raw; or apply externally in ointments on very small area only. This will give you the opportunity to diagnose a possible propolis allergy in time to eliminate it later when using other methods.

Propolis should not be used:

- Weak body
- Inefficient absorption
- Obstacles on the way to the target areas
- Incorrect administration

Administrations

Propolis can be administered internally: by mouth through extracts, solids, or respiratory inhalations; or through suppositories.

You can use it externally with tinctures, the propolis butter or soft propolis in lotions, etc.

The above administration methods for propolis can be used alone or combined with other natural products, like honey, garlic, ginseng, etc.

Dosages

Dosage will vary with each individual and as the tolerance to propolis is pretty high, even 1 g per Kg of body weight per day. But take into consideration the age of each individual and their state of health. Raw propolis, 3-10 g a day, can be swallowed after 5-20 minutes of chewing. This will stain your teeth but brushing with 95% grain alcohol will clean them. Propolis tincture of 5-50% can vary from 5 to 30 drops, three times a day, between meals, in a tablespoon of water or tea.

Start with low doses using several methods like in honey, capsules, creams, suppositories; and use several types of propolis extracts, like water, alcohol, fat extracts, etc.

If you buy commercial propolis, be sure of the manufacturer's quality control of the product and that it has been tested for contaminants. Also check for expiration date. Store all your propolis products, especially the solutions and/or the preparations in a cool, dark place.

~

Harvesting Propolis

Figure 5.4: The cover is left open a little to increase ventilation and let light in. This stimulates the bees to seal the slots with propolis.

Use a fine inner screen as an inner screen cover and set it on the edge of the inner cover. The picture to the left has an exaggerated opening, but you get the idea. It is to let in light that forces the bees to propolise the inner screen. The finer the mesh in the screen, the purer the propolis will be. The larger the mesh, or holes if you use plastic, the more wax you will get. I just place the edge of the lid on the edge of the box. Photo: FOA *Value-added products from beekeeping*, Bulletin 124

Another way of harvesting propolis is using the good-grade fine mesh landscape fabric made out of nylon. Cut a piece to fit the top and overlap the box edges by an inch. This may stick to the edges and make noises when pulling it off. You roll up the fiber and place it into a plastic bag without folding against the roll. When you are ready to work with it, take it out of the freezer and unroll it over plastic wrap or wax paper.

Caution here: taking too much propolis will reduce the bees' protection. Don't take propolis from between the hive boxes if you use the Langstroth hive. Use discretion.

~

Recipes and Preparations

1. Mouth Wash: Use a combination of 80% water propolis extract, 15% mineral water, 1% soft propolis extract, 2% essential oils (mint oil, eucalyptus oil, rosemary oil, sage oil, lavender oil etc.), and 2% honey.[66]

2. Capsules: You can add raw propolis, propolis butter, soft propolis, or propolis oil in your capsules. What you need to do is find and buy large amounts of empty capsules, 00 is the usual size, and an encapsulator. Major herb companies would have the capsules and encapsulator.

3. Powder from raw propolis: When you have gathered the propolis from your hives, place it in a pan of water and shake it. All wood, dead insects, bee parts, etc. will float to the surface. Skim the surface to remove the "debris" and drain the water. You can use a dehydrator on low to dry it. Once dried, place it in a freezer. When you want to use it in powder form, after 1-2 days in the freezer, grind it in a coffee grinder to get a fine powder. Do this fast as speed of the grinder will also force the wax and resins to clump up. If you use a heated grinder, the wax in the propolis will gum up. Store your propolis in a dark container. I suggest you grind the powder as you need it.

4. Inhalations: Insert 30% propolis tincture, 10-30 drops into a liter of simmering water. Inhale the vapors for about 3-5 minutes. Putting in Thyme herb may also help with headaches.

5. Add Propolis to Honey.

---

[66] http://www.ncbi.nlm.nih.gov/pmc/articles/PMC3183661/. This study was carried out to investigate the effectiveness of a propolis-containing mouth rinse in inhibition of plaque formation and improvement of gingival health. Vidya Dodwad and Bhavna Jha Kukreja Indian Society Periodontology, 2011

6. Spray – 10% propolis tincture. If the spray hole is plugged, press several times and/or agitate the container, the alcohol from the solution will dissolve the propolis clot that is plugging the hole.

7. You can encapsulate propolis powder in 00 capsules; Put into homemade chewing gum reminding again, it will stain teeth; make a glyceride, use in suppositories, put it in smoothies….

There are actually only 4 recipes you need to work with for propolis.

1 Propolis in Coconut Oil (called Propolis Butter): 2 Tbsps of Propolis pdr. And 1/4 cup of Coconut Oil. Melt in a double boiler on low-medium heat until propolis is dissolved. About 40 minutes. Cool. If there are any propolis pieces left, or if it separates, stir them in even after the mixture sets. Coconut oil turns semi-solid after stirring it. You can take up to .2 oz. 4 times a day. You can use ½ tsp per day.

The picture to the right is the above recipe multiplied 4 times then 2 Tbsps of propolis added. Stick to the recipe as this is too thick.

If you want to use this in cosmetics, you add 2 Tbsp of propolis pdr. to 1 cup of Coconut Oil, heat and stir. This should be liquid enough to actually blend in with the rest of your ingredients. The amount you use would depend on your purpose. It if is a healing salve: add 1 Tbsp of more liquid propolis butter to 1 cup of your salve recipe. You can also use it alone for burns, wounds, abscesses….

The idea behind using Coconut Oil is that it doesn't go rancid. I buy 65# every couple years from Tropical Tradition for cooking, classes, my formulas, etc. Yes, it is expensive, but I believe in quality. In the long run, it saves me money buying it in bulk.

This butter recipe is one we use as our practicums in the Apitherapy Class. We had a dab left when one of the students came up and showed me a rash she had on her arm made by a metallic bracelet. We rubbed a tiny amount on her arm. Before the class ended that day, the rash was gone.

2   Propolis alcohol tincture: The tincture is the most common propolis preparation, easy to make by everyone and having maximum therapeutic effect. You make soft propolis extract from the tincture. From the soft propolis, you can make hundreds or even thousands of other preparations and/or products.

I make my tincture by putting 1 part of propolis powder in a dark, glass container and adding about 2 parts of 90-96% grain alcohol. Shake daily as often as you remember for 2 weeks or longer then strain. This may come to about 30% -/+ of tincture.

After straining add 1 part of propolis and 10 parts 90-96% grain alcohol. Leave in container for 2-3 months before straining. The second extract will not have the same grade as the first extract. You can add the two together or use the second extract to coat the inside of your hives.

For 10% extraction: 1 part (100 g) propolis pdr. to 9 parts (900 g or 1 kg) ethanol alcohol (grain alcohol).

For 5% extraction: 1 part (100 g) propolis pdr. to 18 parts (1900 g or 19 kg) ethanol alcohol (grain alcohol).

Alcohol tinctures are used for inhalers.

3   Water tincture: Soak propolis for several days or boil it in water. The yield of active ingredients is lower than with alcohol, but water extracts have shown to exhibit bactericidal and fungicidal effects. Processing is the same as alcohol tincture.[67]

Water extract:[68]

---

[67] FOA *Value-added products from beekeeping,* bulletin 124
[68] http://www.bee-hexagon.net/files/file/fileE/Health/PropolisBookReview.pdf

o 300 ml (10.1 oz.) of water in a pan with 30 g (1.05 oz.) propolis cut in small pieces. Boil gently for 40-45 min. Cool down, collect wax from the surface and add a another portion of 30 g propolis pieces and another 300 ml of cold water and boil gently for another 10-15 minutes. Cool down, collect wax from the surface. You should have about 500-600 ml of propolis water extract

o Simple extraction with water: Add 50 g (1.76 oz.) of propolis to 100 ml (1.4 oz.) of water. Boil for 60 minutes. Cool down to room temperature and filter. According to Ludyanski this water extract has an antifungal, antibacterial effect, and other known biological effects. This water is ready for drinking. Keep in a dark place.

4 Soft propolis: Put 10% propolis tincture on a plate. Use a blow dryer on low and blow over the propolis until the alcohol has evaporated. This will only take a few minutes and will take on the consistency of dark syrup. If you blow dry it long enough, the water will also dry up and you will be back at the beginning but with a hard clump of propolis. After the propolis settled, I just poured from the brown jar.

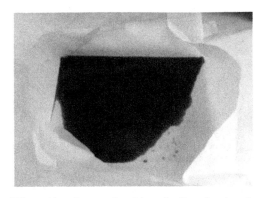 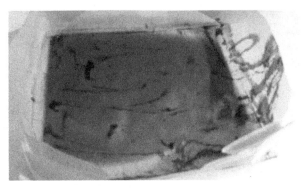

The tincture in the left photo is propolis from Africa; in the right photo is propolis from my hives. Both are 2 oz or 50 g of the 10% Propolis Tincture. I used parchment paper so I could move the propolis around and not soak into the paper. The more air flow, the faster the alcohol; will dry out.

In the 2 pictures on the next page, the one on the left is what it looks like when a hair dryer was used on low (not cold) setting. In less than 10 minutes, the propolis looks like the picture in the right. It will flow flowing like warm honey.

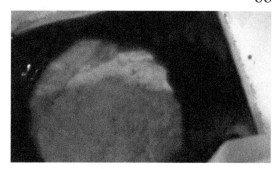 

The above picture shows the propolis tincture from Africa on the left and mine on the right. Both were blowed-dried down to about .5 oz or 13 g of soft propolis. The difference between them is:

Africa	Mine
Tincture 2 weeks old	Tincture 8 days old
Darker	Lighter
Pure propolis pdr.	Pdr. containing wax
More propolis properties	Less propolis properties
Coats the glass	Doesn't coat the glass well

There are a lot of variables going on here, but the main idea is the longer you leave the propolis in the grain alcohol, the more properties you are going to get in your tincture.

Soft propolis can be used in base creams and ointments with emulsifiers.

Propolis is a resin, so clean-up should be with the same alcohol that was used for the tincture. Pour a small of alcohol in a glass bowl and rinse your tools then wash them. The alcohol used to rinse the tools can be used to make more tincture. If you are worried about the germs in the kitchen … think about it.

Other than chewing it whole, the previous 4 recipes can be used in most anything you wish to create.

My Ultimate Smoothie

All organic and put into a blender
- 1 Tbsp Chia seed
- 1 Tbsp Walnuts (omega fats)
- 1 Tbsp pumpkin seeds (worms don't like the green pigment)
- 1 Tbsp Hemp seed
- 1 tsp of Propolis Butter
- About 12 almonds
- 1 Tbsp roasted seed butter or nut butter (for taste)
  Enough water to blend everything to a paste.

Add while blender is running:
- 1 scoop of Green pdr. (greens to cleanse the liver)
- ½ tsp Spirulina pdr.
- ½ Tbsp – 1 Tbsp raw honey
- A handful of blueberries, strawberries, cranberries, frozen. If fresh, add an ice cube.
- 1 Tbsp of bee pollen

Blend until everything is smooth, adding more cold water if necessary.

Chapter 9

Bee Venom Therapy

Bee Bread is the main source for the production of Bee venom. It is produced by 2 glands associated with the sting apparatus in the worker with production increasing in the first 2 weeks of the adult worker and reaching a maximum when the worker becomes a guard. Venom is at the highest in the queen upon her emergence. The drones have no such glands, so they don't have stingers either.

© Can Stock Photo - csp1063438

The active component in bee venom is the 50% Mellitin. It has powerful anti-inflammatory, anti-bacterial, and anti-viral actions. The other 50% of bee venom is a complex mix of a variety of peptides and proteins, some of which have strong neurotoxic and immunogenic effects. Photo: https://www.pinterest.com/pin/3237030956331547

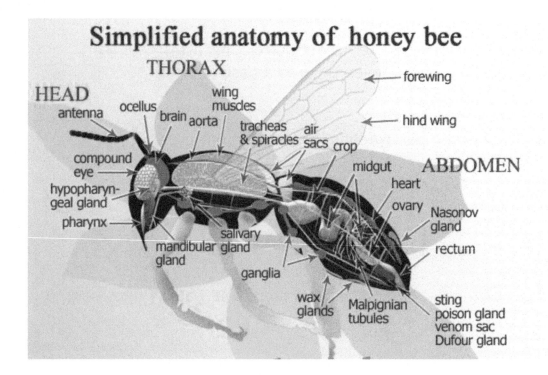

Simplified anatomy of honey bee

69

_____

69 http://www.geochembio.com/biology/organisms/honeybee/#image

The 3 parts of a stinger are the stylus and the 2 barbed slides (or lancets), one on either side of the stylus. The stinger is not pushed in by the bee but is drawn in by the barbed slides. The slides move alternately up and down the stylus so when the barb of one side has caught and retracts, it pulls the stylus and the other barbed  side into the wound. When the other barb has caught, it also retracts up the stylus pulling the sting further in. This process is repeated until the stinger is fully in and even continues after the sting and the stinger is detached from the bee's abdomen. Photo: Stinger vs hypodermic needle, https://www.pinterest.com/pin/3237030956331547

What Bee Venom Is

The Mellitin in bee venom is a protein and all proteins, when heated over 50°C (122°F), would be denatured. Mellitin can tolerate 100°C (212°F) without denaturing.

The enzyme hyaluronidase in bee venom aids the action of the venom by catalyzing the breakdown of protein-polysaccharide complexes in tissue, allowing the venom to penetrate further into the flesh.[70]

Hyaluronidase is also a natural substance found in the body, and is collected from either cows or pigs. It is cleaned to remove animal substances. It may also be produced in a laboratory that recreates it from human albumin sources. Hyaluronidase injection is a spreading substance. It is used with other medicines given under the skin to improve their uptake by the body. This method of drug delivery is only used when the drug cannot be given by injection into a vein. Hyaluronidase injection is used to increase absorption of fluids or medicines that are injected into your skin. It also used to help improve absorption of radioactive substances during a procedure called subcutaneous urography.[71]

Bee venom can be found in two major forms:

- Liquid, as it is immediately after extraction or when it is injected by the bee through her stinger.
- Dried, after collection with special devices (bee venom collectors).

---

[70] http://www.compoundchem.com/2014/08/28/insectvenoms/
[71] http://www.mayoclinic.org/drugs-supplements/hyaluronidase-injection-route-subcutaneous-route/description/drg-20064183

Dr. Michael Simics is one of the world's foremost authorities on bee venom:[72]

Liquid, pure, bee venom:

"Bee venom is a colorless, sharp-bitter tasting liquid with an aromatic odor that is similar to ripe bananas. It is slightly acidic (pH 5.0 to 5.5). Liquid bee venom on blue litmus paper changes the color to red indicating an acidic reaction. However, the aqueous solution of whole dried bee venom does not show this effect, suggesting that volatile compounds create the acidic properties. Bee venom dries at an ambient temperature within about 20 minutes and loses 65% to 70% of its original weight. <u>After the liquid has evaporated, 0.1 mg. of pure whole dried venom can be collected (per bee sting)</u>."

Dried bee venom:

"The pure whole dried venom has a yellowish brown color. The specific weight is 1.313 g/cm3. The toxicity expressed as LD50 is 2.8 mg/kg (mice, i.v.). LD50 means that 50% of the mice will die when 2.8 mg. of venom per kilogram body weight is intravenously injected into them. Bee venom is cold resistant and freezing does not seem to reduce its toxicity. It is also heat resistant when dry, even at 100°C. Dried bee venom, if protected from moisture, can retain its toxic properties for several years."[73]

A.N. Melnichenko & O.V. Kapralova:

"Dried bee venom has a polycrystalline structure. Examinations under the microscope showed that bee venom, as drops of its watery solution dry, assumes characteristic physical structure, the components comprising it being of various forms and sizes. It is not difficult to quickly determine the classification of the venom (bee venom, wasp, hornet, Eve-viper venom) based on physical structure. No chemical combination with some substance or other occurs. Bee venom is not destructible."[74]

---

[72] http://www.beevenom.com/
[73] "Bee Venom, Exploring the Healing Power", 1994, p.12
[74] Munich 1969, at the XXII-Nd. Apimondia Congress

The color of bee venom is visible under natural light; smell and taste are assessed organoleptically; bee venom dissolves totally in distilled water; pH 4.5 – 5.5; and is insoluble in alcohol.

Bee venom is made to defend the bee and its colony. However, the active compounds present in bee venom, in small amounts (equivalent of less than 100-300 bee stings per adult), can be very beneficial to human health.

Bee venom is a potent antioxidant, antifungal, antibacterial, anti-inflammatory, and possesses radio protectant actions. It has been found to exert powerful actions as an antibacterial agent, anti-inflammatory, anti-arthritic, anti-rheumatic, in neurodegenerative disease, as a cardio tonic, an antioxidant, and as a diaphoretic and diuretic. It has also been found to be a strong immunological agent, stimulating the body's protective mechanisms against disease. The Eclectic Botanical physicians considered it to be a potent alterative.

A mature forager bee has in her bee venom sack about 100-150 µg of venom (Schumacher et al., 1989), and young queens about 700 µg (Schmidt, unpublished).

Besides 65-70% water, bee venom is a combination of 18 different components. Dr. Kim M-H. Christopher, one of the greatest experts in BVT in the world, has published in *Bee Informed*, the Journal of the American Apitherapy Society (autumn issue, 1997); the following table shows the major components related to the dried bee venom composition:

Component	Mol. Wt.	% (Dry Venon)	Reference
Peptides			
Melittin	2,840	40-50	Neumann *et al.*, 1952
Apamin	2,036	2-3	Habermann *et al.*, 1965
CD-Peptide 401	2,588	2-3	Fredholm, 1966
Adolapin	11,500	1.0	Shkenderov, 1982
Protease inhibitor	9,000	< 0.8	Shkenderov, 1973
Secarpin		0.5	Gauldie *et al*, 1976
Tertiapin		0.1	Gauldie *et al*, 1976

Melittin F		0.01	Gauldie *et al*, 1976
Procamine A, B		1.4	Nelson & O'Connor, 1968
Minimine	6,000	2-3	Lowy *et al*, 1971
Cardio EP		< 0.7	Vick *et al*, 1974

Enzymes			
Hyaluronidase	38,000	1.5-2.0	Neumann & Habermann
Phospholipase A2	19,000	10-12	Habermann & Neumann, 1957
lucosidase	170,000	0.6	Shkenderov *et al*, 1979
Acid Phosphomonoestee	55,000	1.0	Shkenderov *et al*, 1979
Lysophospholipase	22,000	1.0	Ivanova *et al*, 1982

Active Amines		
Histamine		
Dopamine	0.13-1.0	Owen, 171
Norepinephrine	0.1-0.7	Owen, 1982

Non-Peptide Components		
Carbohydrates: Glucose & Fructose	<2.0	O'Connor *et al*, 1967

Lipids		
6 Phospholipids	4.5	O'Connor *et al*, 1967

Amino-Acids		
R-Aminobutyric Acid	< 0.5	Nelson & O'Connor, 1968
B-Aminoisobutyric acid	< 0.01	Nelson & O'Connor, 1968

Bee Venom Is Good For[75]

- Antibiotic, antibacterial
- Anti-inflammatory (there is a polypeptide called Mast Cell Degranulating peptide that has 100 fold stronger anti-inflammatory activity than hydrocortisone (Orlov).
- Cytostatic effect – suppresses certain stages of cell division (tumor growth) (Forester). Charles Mraz shares a story of a man with a tumor

---

[75] Dr. Stefan Stangaciu, www.apitherapy.com AIC

on his lip. When it was stung once, the tumor disappeared and never came back.

- General prophylactic (prevent diseases) properties (yoirich).
- Improves general condition of the body (potchinkova).
- Protects the body against x-rays (orlov/brooks).
- Negative, toxic effects (large doses).
- Antibiotic properties
- Heart in medium doses:
- Blood and blood vessels:
- Immune system:
- Nervous system:
- Endocrine system:
  - The release of histamine always occurs prior to the release of epinephrine and nor-epinephrine (Brooks *et al*).
  - After B.V. injection (30-60 seconds) plasma histamine levels increase approximately 20-30 times.
  - 5 to 10 minutes after B.V. injection, both levels of epinephrine and nor-epinephrine increase 10 times then slowly fall to control in 30 to 90 minutes (like in stress reaction), but without no major cardiovascular-respiratory changes (Brooks *et al*).
  - Stimulates and intensifies the activity of the Pituitary Adrenal System (increases the cortisol in blood and 17 ketosteroids in the urine (Guseva/Artemov).
  - B.V. and two of its components (melittin and the cardio EP fraction) produce sharp and sustained elevation in circulating cortisol (Brooks *et al*).
  - The increase of cortisol level is inhibited by the absence of Vitamin C in the diet (Brooks *et al*).
  - The effects are stronger on younger study animals (dogs) compared to older ones (Brooks *et al*).

Dr. Bodog Beck, *The Bible of Bee Venom Therapy*, wrote:

"The curative value of bee venom is due mainly to its hemorrhagic and neurotoxic properties - especially to the former.

The *hemorrhagic effect* of the bee venom is not only a powerful action on the blood itself, stimulating the circulation, but also on the blood vessels. This is the best explanation and interpretation of its efficiency. *Bee venom accelerates and intensifies the circulation, and dilates the capillary vessels.* It has a distinct endotheliolytic action, to such an extent that *it opens the capillary walls, enabling the blood cells to transmigrate into the tissues.* This will result in an increased metabolism and, on account of the greater supply of oxygen, in an adequate oxidation, addition heat supply, improved elimination of accumulated waste, and destruction of bacterial growth – in other words, bee venom will produce exactly the effects which are required to correct the existing harmful pathological conditions and to restore the disturbed normal physiological state."

I expect dilating the blood vessels is why women's monthly cycles are heavier than usual when they are stung.

He goes on to write:

"The longer the time which has elapsed from the introduction of the toxin, the less effective the antitoxin will be, and it may prove even useless….

"Another essential law of immunity is, *it wears off, as it is very seldom absolute.* It is an interesting phase of this retrogression that the longer the time required for acquisition of immunity, the more permanent is is; rapid immunization is quickly lost. We know that if beekeepers who have acquired immunity are not stung for a certain period they will find that it has partly or considerably diminished or has been entirely lost. Of course, this depends on the degree acquired and on the length of time which has elapsed….

"We must not forget that by immunity to bee stings we literally mean that a person loses his sensitivity toward the toxic effects of bee venom."

I have been stung enough that there is pain at the initial site in the beginning, but the pain is gone within minutes and the swelling and redness is gone in less than 20-30 minutes. No signs of anything. However, the effect of BV is still powerful. I also take 3,000 Vitamin C with bioflavonoids to help my adrenal gland produce the needed cortisol.

B.V. Negative Effects

- Allergic reactions to people with high sensitivity to the hymenopteran venoms (0.5 – 2% of the people): general pruritus, nettle rash, myxoedema, spasms of the smooth muscles; sudden decrease of blood pressure - colaps (Orlov).
- The histamine content of B.V. may cause spasms of the coronary vessels (according to Uspenski and others) when high dosage of B.V. is present.
- 200 - 300 Simultaneous stings poison an individual by affecting Cardiovascular, Respiratory, and Nervous System: shortness of breath, cyanosis, quickening of the pulse, convulsions, paralysis.
- 500 or more stings cause death through paralysis of the respiratory center.

Itching usually shows a good therapeutic result (Forestier, Palmer).

Bee Venom Indications

Bee venom, the fire related bee product according to acupuncturists, is very beneficial in all sorts of cold related diseases like arthritis, cancers, MS, Raynaud disease. It is also beneficial in different tissues, organs, and systems that are sluggish.

Another way to better understand the BV indications is if looking at a good anatomy and physiology book, there are two main nervous systems:

- Sympathetic: generally an activator.
- Parasympathetic: used to "calm down, sleep, eating and digestion" system.

Almost 50% of the diseases in humans and animals can be considered having too little sympathetic activities and/or too much parasympathetic. As a result, the body becomes heavy, cold, and more or less inert in whole or in part, with or without long standing pains. Bee venom is an excellent sympathetic nervous system activator.

A person who practices BVT will feel and see step by step that his/her body becomes alive again. The body is warmer and moves painlessly faster with easier movement. If the disease is localized, for example a skin tumor or arterial or vein thrombosis, BVT will very likely bring balance and health to the area, especially if the apitherapist is competent at his/her job.

Some of the BV indications established by apitherapy specialists from all over the world are:

Cardiovascular diseases (cardiology): You need to be cautious here if the individual is on Beta Blockers or any heart/cardio medications. If they go into shock, the epipen may be adversely effective.

Musculoskeletal system diseases

Nervous system diseases (neurology)

Eye diseases (ophthalmology)

Skin diseases (dermatology)

Endocrine system diseases

Genital apparatus diseases (Gynecology)

Immune system diseases

Viral diseases

Cancers (oncology)

Allergies: Desensitization for BV Allergy, Bodog Beck.

Bee Venom Administration and Techniques

When you are doing a sting test, pull the stinger out of the bee (or use a sting mesh) and do a micro sting on the right fore arm. Wait 20-30 minutes. If no there is no reaction other than a little redness and/or swelling, chances are the person can take bee stings. But always use the right forearm because the skin is tough and the skin is not as sensitive as other parts of the body and it's the farthest away from the heart.

There are 3 reasons for stinging:

- Apipuncture – the process of using stingers on acupuncture points.
- Stinging spots for certain reasons – knee for arthritis, scars, sore points, etc. The picture to the right is stinging for scars from melanoma surgery.
- Along the spine for Lyme disease.

BVT is administered by three methods:

- Stings: Pure bee venom, administered through micro, half, or full bee stings. The most effective method.
- Bee venom solutions: administered through injections by a licensed professional.
  - Bee venom ointments/liniments: administered usually through simple local application, massages and/or acupressure or through special physiotherapeutic methods like iontophoresis (the introduction through electric currents, of ions of soluble salts into the tissues of the body, often for therapeutic purposes).

  For BV injections, contact:
  Dr. Michael Simics
  Apitronic Services
  9611 No. 4 Road, Richmond, BC, V7A 2Z1, Canada
  Ph/Fax: (+604) 271-9414
  E-mail: msimics@direct.ca
  Website: http://www.beevenom.com

- Other methods of administration not sufficiently investigated by scientists and clinicians that are rarely used but can be practiced usually only by medical doctors specialized in apitherapy are:
  - Per os (through the mouth): bee venom tablets; bee venom combined with honey; or bee venom in homeopathic granules.
  - Inhalations (through the respiratory apparatus). Can be potentially very dangerous.
  - Intra-muscular, intra-articular injections, which have been proven in practice as not being as effective as the intradermal injections.

○ Intravenous bee stings as in the BVT[76] for varicose veins.

BVT can be administered alone or in combination with other healing methods. A simple sting or bee venom injection will do almost nothing beneficial for our health if used alone. You must take care of nutrition, blood flow and quality, nervous and endocrine system, body's general structure, mental, emotional, and psychological characteristics. It is always a good idea to study and use other alternative healing methods as described in Chapter 2 as much as possible in conjunction with BVT.

Performing BVT

I have my people fill out an 8-page personal history form, which is in the document section of this book. After we discuss the form for 3 hrs, I know their diet, emotional state, medications, supplements, everything but if they are allergic to bee stings, unless stated in the form. If they have never been around bees or never stung by a bee, I ask them to take 1 grain of bee pollen and work their way up to a Tbsp. If they can tolerate bee pollen, which will have most of the chemical components in BV except melittin, then we will do a micro bee sting first.

What You Should Do

1 Be sure that you have all anti-allergy means close to you, like Benadryl lotion or tablets, epipen (most important), anti-sting salves, etc.

2 There is a multi-sting mesh available for micro stings that will allow the bee to keep her stinger.

3 Everyone has a fear of bee stings the first time. Take the time to talk to your patient, go over the paperwork to familiarize yourself with their history and interject personal questions. This is the time they need to build trust in you and for you to get to know them. Interject some humor to help relax the muscles, tension, and stress. Show them the bee and be honest about the sting hurting. I have not seen it not hurt, so don't treat them like children.

---

[76] BVT = Bee venom therapy.

4 All the while you are working with them you share what you are doing in a soft, modulated tone of voice. This has a calming effect and no one really likes surprises. Let them know when you use a soapy wash towel when you wipe down the area; when you dry; when you touch to discern sting sites; before the sting, describe what you are doing; and when you wipe them after the sting. Before every task, you let them know a couple seconds before each task. This can help them relax the area. This will establish trust like nothing else will.

5 Have the individual lie still if they are comfortable, and if not have them sit up on the table, and ask how they are doing at every step so you can establish a level of comfort for them. After a couple sessions, you won't have to do this as often because they will know what to expect. Keep them at least 20-45 minutes after the first sting to see what kind of reaction there will be. This is a good time to tell gentle jokes to again relax their muscles, tension, blood pressure, etc. Touching and massaging the sting site after BVT will stimulate the venom to move and relax the person.

6 If any signs of allergy occur, immediately use the anti-allergic drugs and/or methods known to you.

7 A good reaction is when the individual, usually after several BVT sessions, tells you that the places where he/she has been stung have started to itch. Advise the BVT recipient NOT to scratch the skin, because this will worsen the itching. Use lotion on the skin or a cold pack.

8 During each session, try to sting other active, painful points (spots). Especially at the beginning of BVT, never sting, the anterior parts of the body, parts where the skin is usually whiter, softer and have less hair as it can lead to the greatest risk of allergies. Fair-skinned people are more sensitive to pain and stings than darker skin people.

9 In apipuncture (a term used indicating one is using stingers instead of needles) sting only the yang areas of patient's body: the back, from buttocks up to the shoulder blades; the posterior-lateral parts of the hands, fore-arms, elbows, arms, shoulders; the upper part of the feet, the anterior-lateral and posterior part of the calves, knees and thighs.

Stinging all other body areas can result in a higher risk of allergy and/or adverse reactions.

10 Give them something to drink and recommend hydration before each session and start them on Vitamin C with bioflavonoids to help the body create more cortisol for the adrenaline gland.

11 Study the BVT recipient's tongue before each BVT session. If the tongue is dried, it has teeth marks at its edges, or if it's too red and/or has speedy micro-contractions, especially at its tip, do NOT administer BVT. these signs show an excess functioning of the orthosympathetic (autonomic nervous system). BVT strongly increases the same part of the nervous system.

12 Before BVT, study the recipient's pulse. If it is too high, over 90 beats/second or too low, under 60 beats, do not offer BVT. If the pulse is irregular do NOT offer BVT. Wait until the pulse has a regular beat.

Michael Broffman, a licensed acupuncturist and apitherapist from California, wrote the following BVT related rules for Bee Informed:[77]

DO promote the use of BVT.
DON'T over-sell BVT as a cure.

DO provide assistance to those inquiring about BVT.
DON'T recommend starting BVT without help from an experienced assistant.

DO send information on what to expect during BVT.
DON'T encourage self-treatment without full understanding of the proper procedure.

DO include information on risks and reactions during BVT.
DON'T suggest that full benefit always occurs right away without some adverse temporary reaction.

DO make it clear that relief from symptoms depends on each individual.

---

[77] The American Apitherapy Society's former journal; more details in www.Apitherapy.org

DON'T promise immediate results.

DO advise the importance of test sting before BVT.

DON'T recommend BVT without test sting even if the person says that they have been stung by bees before.

DO test also the person or spouse doing the treatment and others handling the bees.
DON'T forget that the spouse or new person doing stings may also be allergic.

DO insist on the presence of a sting kit during test sting as well as during the entire treatment.
DON'T expose or subject yourself to liability or risk without a bee-sting kit being present.

The apitherapist must be in control and know what (s)he is doing, remaining calm in any situation. Among all Apitherapy techniques, BVT is the most powerful but also potentially the most dangerous.

Contraindications[78]

- Bee Venom Allergy
- Cardiovascular Diseases
- Metabolic Diseases - insulin dependant Diabetes. BV increases the glucose level in the blood through an increase in corticosteroids secretion which activates the glycogenolysis.
- Malnutrition
- Lung Diseases
- Tuberculosis
- Lung insufficiencies (advanced stages)
- Infecto-Contagious Diseases:
- Feverish diseases
- Flu: Exception is when BV is administered in small amounts in form of ointment and/or through the Japanese micro-apipuncture method).
- Purulent infections
- Tuberculosis

---

[78] Dr. Stefan Stangicu, www.apitherapy.com

- Venereal diseases
- Adrenal Glands Insufficiency
- Kidney Insufficiency
- Glomerulonephritis (acute inflammation of the kidney, typically caused by an immune response.)
- Nephritis
- Polycystic Kidneys
- Albuminuria
- Prostate Diseases: enlarged prostate
- Liver Diseases: Hepatitis
- Eye Diseases: Glaucoma
- Pregnancy
- During Menstruation, periods
- During Full Moon
- During Storms, rain with lightning
- Nursing - Breast Feeding
- Children Under 12 Years Of Age
- Chronic Fatigue Syndrome, advanced stages
- Very Weak Patients
- Too Old And Weak Patients
- Chronic Consumptive diseases
- Alcoholism - Drug addictions
- Mental Disorders
- Excessive hyperfunctions (General Or Local)
- Immediately before or after meals

Except for the real bee venom allergies which lead to respiratory problems and can be proven with blood tests, all of the contraindications mentioned above are more or less relative.

BV creams may also aid in determining allergies if administered in small amounts.

Bee venom cannot heal or improve the conditions of people with low energy level, especially if there is an issue with the adrenal glands.

If someone is an addict, smoker, alcoholic, proceed with caution as the body is already worn out. BV may wear the body out faster from the reactions to the venom.

Home Remedies for Bee Venom Adverse Reactions

Mild reactions: Redness, mild swelling, and heat in the area of the sting site. Photo: Lady Spirit Moon

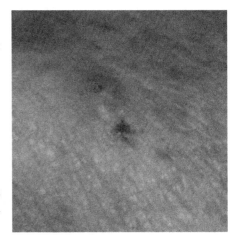

- Apply an ice cube, cold compress, household ammonia, or baking soda applied as a paste.
- Propolis Cream - apply to the skin
- Propolis Tincture: 5-15 drops 3-4 times per day to be taken internally with honey and a cup of tea (or warm water).
- Preparation H Cream (anti-itch cream with hydrocortisone 1%) - Apply to the skin in the area of the sting.
- Bee Sting Lotion - Mix 100 ml water, 5 ml vinegar, and 5 ml salt. Apply this solution to the affected area, repeat as needed.

Moderate reactions: Fever, nausea, fatigue or flu-like symptoms. Photo: Lady Spirit Moon

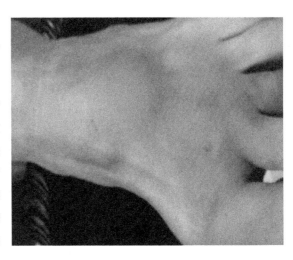

- Ask your local pharmacist and/or medical doctor what are the best anti-allergy preparations available in your nearest pharmacy. They may suggest you to use products like Benadryl Liquid or Claritin - to be taken orally according to the manufacturer's instructions.
- Benadryl Tablets - 50 mg immediately after a bee sting and 4 X 25 mg within the next 24 hours.
- Benadryl Cream - To be applied to the skin on the area of the sting.

Benadryl will also lesson the effect of BVT.

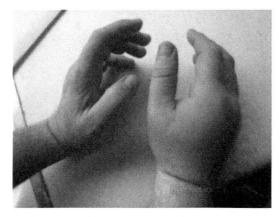

Left: 20 minutes with ice will take the swelling down and last for hours. Photo: www.pinterest.com

Right: Mild to moderate - Can happen with those taking antidepressant medications, with Lyme disease. These were not the sting sites.

Rash

Hives

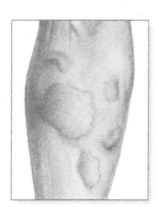

ADAM.

Severe reactions: Anaphylactic Shock, breathing difficulties, extreme swelling, blue lips and fingernails, etc.

- Adrenalin injection ("Anakit" or "Epipen") is used for severe allergic reactions (extreme swelling).
- Should you, your customer, or your BVT recipient have any breathing problems like wheezing, call 911, your family doctor, your allergist, or contact the nearest medical office!

Bee venom is the most potentially dangerous of all bee products.

Every year thousands of people all over the world die because of accidental bee stings, usually an excessive number, as is the case with the Africanized bees, known also by the mass media as "killer" bees. But this usually takes a swarm of bees. A swarm of any species of bees can kill. Horses are especially sensitive to bee stings and have died from just a few stings.

Anytime you start stinging more than 2-3 times a week you need to take 2,000-3,000 mg of Vitamin C with bioflavonoids on a daily basis to help prevent adrenal exhaustion. It takes Vitamin C to create cortisol from the adrenal gland and cortisol is the hormone that is stimulated by the inflammation created by the Melittin in the BV.

~

Management of Bees for BVT

If you are already a beekeeper, then you have no problem as far as managing the bees are concerned. If you are not a beekeeper, then things are somewhat more complicated because you need to purchase the bees and the temporary box in which they must be confined. You will be responsible for their nutrition, hygiene, and health.

Pat Wagner, a well-known Apitherapist from USA (specialized in the treatment of MS) writes:

"Keep Honeybees in a jar for about 1 1/2 to 2 weeks: Get an empty jar (for example, mayonnaise or pickle jars are acceptable). Simply wash the jar with warm water only. Put holes in the lid so that the bees can get plenty of air. Put a teaspoon or two of honey in the bottom of the jar. Place a single layer of tissue paper over the honey. Ask the beekeeper to put some bees (50-75) in the jar and put the top on. Cut an inverted V in the end of an empty toilet paper roll. Hit the jar on your palm to knock the bees to the bottom. Quickly open the lid, insert the empty toilet paper roll, and replace lid. Place the jar of bees in a cupboard or dark, undisturbed place. In a day or so your bees will be calmer which will enable you to retrieve them from the jar. Get a pair of long tweezers (six inches are preferred). I use reverse tweezers – they hold the bee so you don't to squeeze.

"Give Yourself A "Test" sting: Find a place near a sunlit window. Bees go there when they get loose. If the bees are too active, just let a few go to the window and retrieve them at your leisure. With your tweezers, grasp a bee by the head or thorax. Have the honeybee sting you, perhaps on your knee or forearm. Wait approximately fifteen or twenty minutes. Should you encounter difficulty breathing in that time, or other signs of anaphylactic shock, call 911 then use your Epipen kit. "Ice can be used on the sting location both before and after, if needed. Place the bee on the location to be stung; discard the bee after it stings. (Ed. Note: save the bee in alcohol and use it for Apilarnil.) Continue with the remainder of the stings required for that day. Leave the stingers in for no more than 4 minutes.

"To remove the stinger: Grasp the stinger with your tweezers and slide it along the skin. If you don't get the entire stinger out, your body will take care of it. (Ed note: do your best to get the stinger out. Sometimes the sting site may get infected.)

"Remember To Feed The Bees: Just give them a drop or two of honey every couple of days. A fine misting of water is also good."

If possible, let your bees fly every evening for colon cleansing, if their "mother-colony" is over 5 miles far away. Once established in their home for a few days, the bees will fly back to their Bee Buddy. The queen's pheromone is what unites a colony and wears off in a day or two. This is how long it takes for a bee to become accustomed to his new home.

The bee buddy to the left in the picture below was purchased from Harris Apiary. The corrugated paper box connected to the Bee Buddy is the bee's "outhouse" made by a friend who stings himself for Lyme disease. The "outhouse" allows bees to fly out of their living environment and do a cleansing flight when the weather will not allow them to go out of the Bee Buddy. My friend said the bees are much happier.

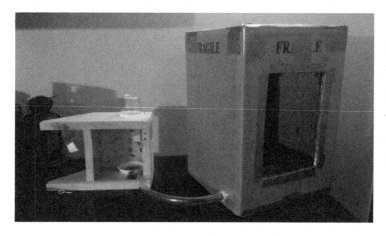

If you have your own bees you can make a mouth vac like mine in the picture on the next page to get your bees as you need them. The materials you need are:

- A wide-mouth half-pint jar, a wide-mouth canning lids, and 1 ring.
- A 5" piece of polypropylene screen mesh.
- A 15" and a 10" plastic tubing, 5/8 OD.
- A cork to fit into one end of 10" tube.
- #8 Aluminium screen mesh, cut about 1" square to shove into the 15" tube.

Drill a 5/8" hole into one into the top of the wide-mouth canning lid as shown in the picture and another opposite it. Sand the metal burrs off both sides of the lid. The holes are for the 2 plastic tubes and they will fit tight.

Shove the 1" square piece of #8 metal hardware cloth into one end of the 15" tube far enough so your lips won't touch the wire. This wire prevents the bees from coming into your mouth. The other end of this tube will go into the hole near the edge. The second 10" tube with a cork goes into the other hole. The cork is to prevent the bees from leaving the jar once captured.

Screw on the wide-mouth band over the 5" polypropylene mesh. Cut a slit into the polypropylene mesh close to the edge of the ring large enough to insert the 15" tube with the wire in it. You may want to position the lid with the 2 large holes on top to mark for the slit before inserting the tube into the lid. About an inch from the first slit a cut another slit about half the size you cut for the tube, large enough for you to pull out a bee with tweezers. You do it now so you don't have to try to do it with bees in the jar.

Place some crystalized honey on the bottom. If it's liquid honey, put a small piece of tissue over the honey to prevent the bees from taking a bath in it. When you go to get the bees, use your thumb to hold the lid with the 2 large holes firmly against the top of the jar ring with your 4 fingers on the bottom to form a seal. Apply pressure to be sure there is no air gap under the lid with the 2 holes. Push the longest tube into the lid and through the largest slit, leaving the e end for your mouth. This is the tube you will use to gently inhale the bees into the jar. Remove the cork and push the second tube into the second hole just enough to hold the tube.

While firmly holding onto the lid between your thumb and 4 fingers, bend down over the hive entrance. You want guard bees as they have the strongest venom. Place your mouth over the tube with the wire, point the other tube close to a bee and very gently inhale. The bee will come into the jar if the lid is held firm enough. The lid held to the top rim of the band seals it and allows you to suck out the air in the jar as you take in a bee. Continue until you have enough bees. If you wish you put in a little honey to calm them. If you inhale too deeply, too fast, or too hard, the bees will hit the side of jar and may die from the impact.

When you have enough bees, you remove the lid with both tubes and place a piece of masking tape over the 2 slits in the polypropylene screen. Put in a couple drops of water. When you need a bee, push the tweezers in the smaller hole you cut earlier, grab your bee, and gently pull her out. Put a piece of small masking tape over the hole when you are done. The other lid with many air holes is for when you want to transport the bees. Just remove the band while holding onto the polypropylene mesh, place the multi-holed on top and screw on the band. On the other hand, I just transport them with the mesh.

Removing a stinger for micro stings
Photos: 3 Dr. Stefan Stangaciu

If you are using a sting mesh, follow the directions that come with it. If you are going to pull out the stinger, follow the directions below.

Grasp the bee by the thorax. If you grab the abdomen you will squeeze out the abdomen's contents. If you need to, reposition the bee to grab the thorax.

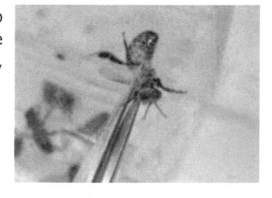

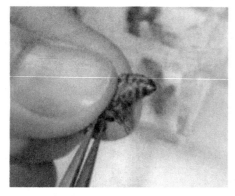

Gently grasp the bee so you can gently massage her abdomen if you need to.

Pull the stinger out quickly. If not done quickly, her whole insides will come with the stinger.

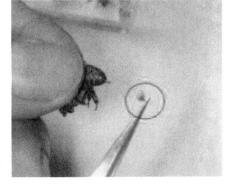

Using the tip of the tweezers that are flat on the end, grab the stinger as in the photo to the left. Do not grab the venom sac. Firmly push the stinger into the skin.

If this is a micro sting, push the stinger into the skin and pull it out immediately. If it is a half sting, push it in, count to 20-30 seconds then pull out the stinger. 90% of the venom will disburse in the first 2-3 minutes. The other 10% will disburse in the next minute or 2. Leaving the stinger in longer only irritates the skin. The stinger is a foreign object.

You don't usually use a lot of bees for micros, though you will if the stinger is used for only one sting. It is suggested you not use a stinger more than 16 times. Not sure from where that number came, but it is about the most I can get without damaging the stinger or dulling it.

Micro stings are excellent for testing but also for facial scars. Experience has shown that the thick fiber forming the scar will not allow the venom to travel through the scar, so you sting along the edges of the scar and the venom will attack from below. It breaks down the skin and rejuvenates it. Eventually the scar will get smaller. When you get enough stings, as in the case of Lyme disease, you will see small facial scars disappear on their own. Just goes to show how BV travels.

Using the Entire Bee

Once you know where you are going to sting, either by touch or using a medical pen and marking the spot, place the bee on the skin and gently drag her body across the spot. If she doesn't set down the stinger, gently touch the top of her abdomen to force the stinger in. Once the stinger is in the skin,

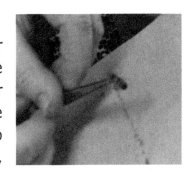

pull the bee quickly to the side. You want to try to prevent her intestines from coming out with the venom sac. Photo: Lady Spirit Moon

NOTE: I suggest after stinging you put the bees in a glass container and cover them with alcohol. Slosh them around to kill them instantly. The bee will take on a rotting smell because the alcohol will not thoroughly penetrate the bee. So you need to mash them while in the alcohol then use then the bee tincture as you would an Apilarnil tincture.

Always cleanse the sting site with soap and water then wipe with a damp cloth. You cannot account for where the bee has been, but you can be sure the skin is clean.

Lyme Disease

Photo: https://en.wikipedia.org/wiki/Ixodes_scapularis

Lyme is a Multi-Systemic Disease caused by the bacteria called Spirochete Borrelia burgdorferi (Bb) which normally is a bacterial spirochete (spiral shape).[79] It is usually transmitted by the bite of the Black Legged Tick, also known as the Deer Tick (*Ixodes Scapularis*). Lyme disease may also be transmitted in utero - from a pregnant mother to her unborn baby.

Borrelia burgdorferi has been found in breast milk but no one knows if it is transmitted through the milk. Other Tick-borne infections have been directly transmitted through the blood supply. As yet, there are no recorded cases of direct transmission of Bb via blood.

Studies vary as to how long the tick must feed on you in order to transmit the disease(s). What is known is the longer an infected tick is embedded in your skin the greater the chance there is to contract diseases.

---

[79] http://www.lymediseaseassociation.org/index.php/about-lyme/medical-lyme/symptom-list

Signs & Symptoms of Lyme disease

Approximately 50% of the patients who contract Lyme disease will remember having a rash. The official name of the rash is Erythema Chronicum Migrans (EM) and it is usually looks like a Bull's Eye in shape. If you have the Bull's Eye Rash then you have Lyme disease![80]

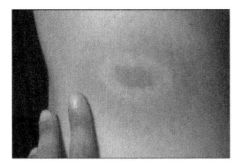

The Erythema Migrans (EM) of Lyme disease can take many forms. The best known is a roughly circular red rash, without itching or pain, which slowly spreads outwards. It may clear in the middle and is often called a bull's eye rash. [81]

The rash may appear on other places on your body other than the bite site (Disseminated disease). It may begin as a single circular red mark that spreads outwards. As it disseminates over the skin it becomes lighter in the area nearer to the center of the bite. In people with darker skin color the rash may appear more like a bruise. The rash is usually not itchy and can be mistaken for a spider bite.[82]

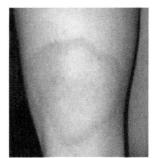

Immediately after an attached tick has been removed from the skin, the site of the bite will continue to be a little red, perhaps for a couple of days; this is not in itself an indication of Lyme disease. The EM develops 2-30 days after the bite.

Other Diseases (Co-infections) with Lyme

The Black Legged Tick (deer Tick) carry other diseases that can accompany Lyme disease. Some of these are:

- Bartonella – Cat Scratch Disease, Trench Fever, and Carrion's Disease). Bartonella bacteria cause several diseases in humans. The three most common are cat scratch disease, caused by *B. henselae*;

---

[80] *Centers for Disease Control & Prevention (CDC) criteria are for surveillance purposes, not diagnosis. According to the CDC surveillance criteria, an erythema migrans (EM) rash in an endemic area means Lyme disease. In a non-endemic area, rash requires a positive test.*
[81] http://www.lymediseaseaction.org.uk/about-lyme/rashes/
[82] Images on the DermIS website

trench fever, caused by *B. quintana*; and Carrión's disease, caused by *B. bacilliformis.*

When using BVT this may appear like stretch marks across the back stemming from the sting site to the sides or across the spine.

- Rocky Mountain spotted fever - Without prompt treatment, Rocky Mountain spotted fever can cause serious damage to internal organs, such as your kidneys and heart.

- Babesia - a malaria-like parasite, also called a "piroplasm," that infects red blood cells. Scientists believe Babesia microti is the most common piroplasm infecting humans, but they have identified over twenty piroplasms carried by ticks. In addition to transmission by a tick, Babesia can be transmitted from mother to unborn child or through a contaminated blood transfusion.

This may appear like a rash in raised spots around the sting site and in several places next to the site. Sometimes these raised spots may connect to each other.

- Malaria – a Lyme victim may also test positive for Malaria.

- Various bowel disorders like IBS (Irritable Bowel Syndrome)

Since Lyme disease is a multi-systemic illness there is a multitude of symptoms associated with the illness.

Some include:

- Flu-like illness
- Fever
- History of tick bite (not all patients recall a bite)
- Headache
- Extreme fatigue
- EM Rash, other rashes (Only found in 50% of patients)
- Malar Flush, Red Ear Lobes
- TMJ (Temporomandibular Join) – jaw pain
- Neck & back pain
- Joint Pain & swelling, bone pain

Note that the rash:

- Does not have to be circular.
- Can become very large (40cm across) with diffuse edges.
- Can be many rashes, not just one.
- Is not necessarily at the site of the tick bite.
- UK studies have shown that around 1 in 3 of people do not see a rash.

Dr. Dietrich Klinghardt, MD, PhD, Klinghardt Academy, 2 Orchard Way, Warren, USA, NJ 07059, website: http://www.klinghardtacademy.com/lyme-disease/: is the leading expert on Lyme disease. His website can cover far more information than I can cover in this book. I strongly suggest you check out his site if you have been diagnosed with Lyme's.

On the next page is the chart used for Lyme disease stinging.

Stinging for Lyme: Photo source: unknown

Spinal Bone	Nerve Supply	Common Warning Signs
C1	Blood supply to the head, pituitary gland, scalp, bones of the face, brain, inner ear and middle ear.	• Headaches •insomnia •high blood pressure • Migraines • chronic fatigue • dizziness
C2	Eyes, ears, sinuses, tongue, forehead	• Sinusitis • ear aches • pain around the eyes • Vision problems • hearing problems
C3	Cheeks, outer ear, face bones, teeth, facial nerves.	• Neuralgia • pimples • eczema
C4	Nose, lips, mouth, Eustachian tube	• Hay fever • runny nose • hearing loss • Adenoids
C5	Vocal cords, neck, glands, pharynx	• Sore throat • laryngitis • hoarseness
C6	Neck muscles, shoulders, tonsils	• Stiff neck • arm pain • tonsillitis • Persistent cough
C7	Thyroid gland, shoulder bursa, elbows	• Bursitis • colds • thyroid conditions
T1	Forearms, hands, wrists, fingers, esophagus, trachea	• Arm and hand pain • difficulty breathing • shortness of breath • asthma
T2	Heart, coronary arteries	• Heart conditions • chest conditions
T3	Lungs, bronchial tubes, pleura, chest	• Bronchitis • pleurisy • pneumonia • congestion
T4	Gallbladder	• Gallbladder conditions • jaundice • shingles
T5	Liver, solar plexus, circulation	• Liver conditions • blood pressure conditions • poor circulation
T6	Stomach	• Indigestion • heartburn • dyspepsia
T7	Pancreas, duodenum	• Ulcers • gastritis
T8	Spleen	• Lower resistance
T9	Adrenal glands	• Allergies • chronic fatigue
T10	Kidneys	• Kidney problems • hardening of the arteries • fatigue • nephritis
T11	Kidneys, ureters	• Skin conditions • eczema • pimples
T12	Small intestines, lymph circulation	• Rheumatism • gas pains
L1	Large intestines, inguinal rings	• Colitis • diarrhea • hernia
L2	Appendix, abdomen, thigh	• Cramps • varicose veins • leg pain
L3	Sex organs, uterus, bladder, knees	• Menstrual pains • irregular periods • miscarriages • impotency • knee pain
L4	Prostate gland, lower back	• Back pain • difficulty, painful or frequent urination
L5	Lower back, buttocks, thighs, legs, feet, sciatic nerve, large intestine	• Back pain • leg pain •constipation
Sacrum	Hip bones, buttocks	• Sacroiliac conditions • back pain • hip pain
Coccyx	Rectum, anus	• Hemorrhoids • tail bone pain

The spine chart on the previous page indicates the spaces between the vertebrae where the stings are placed. You feel for the indentations between the vertebrae or feel for the top of the vertebrae, slide your finger a little either left or right, then down into the indentation between the vertebrae. The stinger is placed about ¾-1" from the center of the spine. You can use a medical pen to mark the spot if you wish or a ballpoint pen.

To repeat, wipe the sting area with a wet cloth containing mild soap. Wipe the area again with a damp towel to wipe off the soap. Dry the area with a dry cloth then mark your sting site again, if necessary.

Picking the bee up at the thorax with tweezers (I use reverse tweezers), place the bottom of the abdomen on the marked area and gently press the abdomen if the bee doesn't sting immediately. Quickly pull the bee to the side to prevent her intestines from coming out with the venom sac.

NOTE: Leave the stinger in the skin for only 4-5 minutes, rather than the 20 minutes acupuncturists will tell you to do on Lyme disease forums. Acupuncture needles are left in the skin for 20 minutes to activate the meridians. The hyaluronidase chemical in the BV moves the venom into the bloodstream, which also moves into the meridians.

A Case History:

I worked with J who came to me with Lyme. Below is his story:

> "On October 11, 2010, I left work early due to a sudden, severe headache that was quite debilitating. Unlike with the migraines I was used to, this headache didn't go away within 24 hours. It was still there the next day, the following week … and it's still here today, although with varying intensity. During the following weeks and months I also noticed an increase in light sensitivity. It became difficult to be outside on sunny days and eventually it got so bad that I had to darken my entire home and ended up spending most of my days living in my basement. Over time I developed other symptoms, too, such as brain fog, fatigue, shaking, balance issues, difficulty walking, depression… For a long time I went from one doctor to another: I saw neurologists, chiropractors, acupuncturists, a pain specialist, massage therapists and other practitioners – with no results. Nobody was able to figure out the root cause of my pain and

instead tried to find medications that might help, but none did. Even heavy painkillers hardly did anything to lower the pain in my head. Finally, after 2 ½ years of being undiagnosed, I decided to get tested for Lyme due to a suspicion that I might have contracted the disease in utero. I tested positive not only for Lyme but Rocky Mountain Spotted Fever, Typhus Fever, Mycoplasma, high levels of HSV 1 and 2 as well as Varicella Zoster and Human Herpes Virus Type 6. I was clinically diagnosed as likely also having Bartonella and Babesia, even though the tests came back negative. After the tests, I started on the usual regimens of first oral and then IV antibiotics in addition to many different types of supplements and other natural remedies. Nothing seemed to help my symptoms. In fact, for a while it seemed like things were only getting worse and I sincerely thought that the disease would eventually take my life. I was completely homebound due to pain and photophobia, often too weak to do anything and too sick to even talk on the phone.

"Then, I read an article about someone who got better from Lyme through BVT. I started researching apitherapy on the Internet and became more and more intrigued by it. I finally decided to give it a try and started stinging in April 2015. I started slowly and over the course of several months worked my way up to 10 stings per session, three times per week.

"Early on in my treatment with BVT, I met Lady, who has been a great help and encouragement along the way. She took the time to review my medical history and supplements and gave me feedback on what to take when and how much. She was gracious enough to allow us and other family members the opportunity to sting under her supervision, guiding us on best practices, everything from catching the bees, to arranging them on tweezers, to learning how to get the bee to sting where we want it to. She taught my wife how to feel for the vertebrae along the spine and how to sting in between them, in order to hit acupuncture points and spread the venom as optimally as possible. She helped us increase from 4 to 8 stings per session, using her intuition and my body's reactions to discern whether I was ready to move up to more stings. She also recommended nutritional changes and herbal solutions to help reduce other symptoms, such as GI troubles, and to support the body during BVT. Even though we live a day's drive away, she was willing to help guide us from a distance, and so my wife has sent her photos after each sting session to show her how my body was reacting, and Lady gives us feedback and loads of encouragement. When I was trying to do too much at once by adding other treatments, Lady recognized that I was overtaxing my system and advised me to slow down, which helped me get my digestive issues back under control and lead to an increase in my good days.

"About two months after starting BVT, in June 2015, I noticed that some of my symptoms had disappeared. I was able to think more clearly and my memory was better; my fatigue was much less severe, I was no longer shaking or having tremors and my balance issues seemed to have gone away. Then, in August, I had my first lower pain day (a 5 instead of a 7, 8 or 9 headache on a scale of 1-10) and actually went out to enjoy life for a few hours. It felt amazing! Since then, these lower pain days have increased in frequency and I have been able to participate in life to a much greater degree. I still have terrible days, where I feel sick and am homebound, but while they used to be the norm, they are now the exception. My light sensitivity is still there but has noticeably improved and I have much more energy than before BVT. For years I was not able to exercise at all. Now I am up to 15 minutes on a treadmill!

"Currently I am 8 months into doing BVT and I keep seeing improvements. I am stinging three times per week (MWF) using 10 bees each time. My wife stings me along the spinal cord, about one inch to the right and left of the spine. I usually ice my back before stinging to decrease the intensity of the pain. We leave the stinger in for 5 minutes. To support my body during this time I take Vitamin C, Magnesium, Vitamin B complex, Grapefruit Seed extract, Milk Thistle, Zinc, Vitamin D, Lymphomax, Quercetin, Turmeric Curcumin, Lithium Orotate, Charcoal, and a Probiotic. For detoxing I use Apple Cider Vinegar and Alka Seltzer Gold. I also take regular Epsom salt baths and use an infrared sauna, when I'm able."

January, 2016, J went to Argentina with his wife. After contacting a beekeeper, his bees were ready for his arrival. He intends to teach others how to sting. He still sends me photos and the reactions are really different. We are not sure if it is the type of bee, the soil and water environment, which can also affect the bee, or what.

As of February 18, 2016 he wrote on Facebook:

"Hello Hive, I care a great deal about sharing hope with fellow Lymies, so here's a bit of an update on my progress. I'm at ten months of BVT and recently went through a flare-up of the pain level of my headache, but it reduced again about 5 days ago - it's now better than the level before the flare.

"I am doing quite well, am out walking or engaging in life every day, especially in the last 5 days. A couple of days ago I walked about 3.5 miles in the morning, after lunch went grocery shopping a few blocks away with my wife, then walked/took the subway to a tango club in the evening. In total I walked 5 or 6 miles, was out until 1am and still felt pretty good the next morning. Today I walked 1 or 2 miles in the morning to go out for coffee, then did a tour of a historic site this afternoon and went for a walk, and am getting ready to go out with friends.

I couldn't have done any of it ten months ago. The photophobia is reducing significantly as well. And could it be that my hair is healthier and fuller? It seems like it. Bee encouraged"

Where to Start With Pictures of Reactions

I always start at T7 (T meaning Thorax) because that is the part of the back that is the toughest from leaning on chairs, clothing rubbing on it, etc. This gets the individual ready for stings on the lower back, which is very sensitive. I never go above T1, and work my way down close to L5 and don't go below. When I get to the bottom, I start back up at the top. The meridian along the spine is called the Governing Channel and its energy runs from top to bottom on the back and bottom to the top on the front. Massage Therapists always work from the top down on the back then up the front from the feet to the head. This is how all the meridian energies flow.

In the beginning when J was stung, his parents, wife, and I all watched as blotches showed on his neck. The places in front of his neck and somewhat on his shoulders that turned red were where lymph nodes would be located. Sometimes these rashes would appear alongside his face.

The photo is 9-2-15.

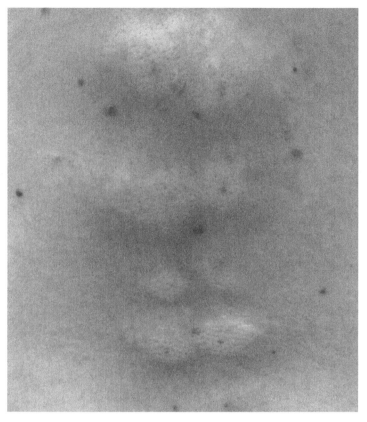

The photo to the left is 2 days later. This is called herxing, named after Jarisch-Herxheimer Herxing, and is believed to occur when injured or dead bacteria release their endotoxins into the blood and tissues faster than the body can comfortably handle it. This is why I put J on Red Clover Blossoms, to keep the blood clean, and Slippery Elm Bark to move the dead bacteria out through the bowels. Slippery Elm Bark encapsulates anything that doesn't belong in digestive tract and moves it out.

In the photo to the right taken 9-15-15 shows what Bartonella may look like when herxing with rashes 15 minutes after the sting.

Bartonella may streak side-to-side across the skin from the site all the across to the side. They look like red stretch marks.

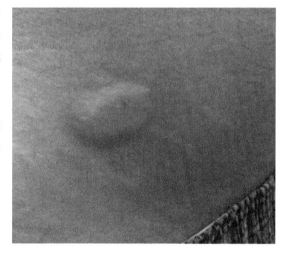

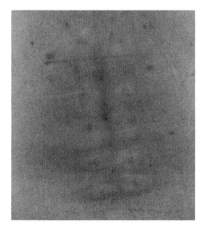

J is still herxing, but the reactions are lessening as seen in the photo to the right taken 12-15-15.

Lyme people have very sensitive skin and feel a lot of pain. They take upwards of 10 stings every other day and take the weekend off. I found that by the time they get to 10 stings and they are about 2-3 months into the program, they get to the point that the stings are almost intolerable. When this occurs, I suggest they just skip 1 session a week for about 3 weeks. By the time they get back to their routine, it will be rough going in the beginning but the body acclimates again and the pain is not as severe.

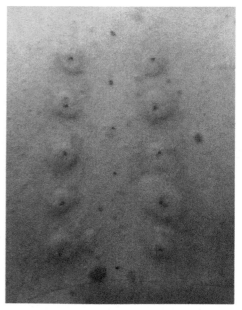

My theory is the skin is very sensitive and it will not tolerate a constant barrage of stings without a letup. The body needs to adjust to each session as it heals and each individual is going to be different. If you push the body beyond its means to acclimate, you will bring in other issues and the healing process will take longer. This is especially true when emotions are involved. One must listen to the body and behave accordingly. Pushing the body beyond its endurance will also slow the healing process.

Chronically ill people are not always aware of their body in terms of what else is going on besides the illness being treated. So this is when you question them at length before each session about any symptoms that may have occurred after the last session.

Another phenomena may appear during BVT called Morgellons. They may appear anywhere on the body shortly after stinging. The medical profession will tell you that it is a figment of the patient's imagination.[83] But I have pulled hair-like fibers out of raised red pimple-like areas - some near the site and one from the side of a man who didn't have Lyme; yet he herxed from all four of his stings during a BVT class demonstration.

We pulled 2 Morgellons out of J at the beginning of his sessions.

---

[83] http://www.mayoclinic.org/morgellons-disease/art-20044996

How Long to Heal from Lyme Disease

It is said that it takes 2 years to kill the Spirochete bacteria and that BVT is the only thing that will kill the bacteria. Whenever I work with people on Lyme disease, I spend several hours counseling them on nutrition, detoxing, how the body works, the importance of being patient, and always … always, always be there for support. Dealing with Lyme can be frustrating and depressing. Knowing there is someone you can call or visit to talk out things, including the anger, will go a long way toward the healing process.

Resources

Live Bees for Stings
Bee Buddies
Ferris Apiary
807 Kings Highway
Yemassee, SC 29945
1-843-717-3089
http://ferrisapiaries.com/?page_id=79

Gaylene Carson – will only gather those bees that freely go into the box. She does not vacuum them out.
Bee Attitudes Apiary & Billy's Goat Hill
Api-Therapy Specialist
1-864-710-3703
130 Timber Trail - Westminster, SC 29693
Like "Billy's Goat Hill" on Facebook!
http://www.billysgoathill.net

Bee venom products and related supplies
Dr. Michael Simics
9611 No. 4 Road,
Richmond, British Columbia,
Canada, V7A 2Z1
Ph./Fax 1-604-271-9414
E-Mail: msimics@direct.ca
Web pages: http://www.direct.ca/beevenom/
http://www.beevenom.com

Apitherapy Organizations
American Apitherapy Society
631-470-9446
www.Apitherapy.org

For online Apitherapy Courses and to join the National Apitherapy Forum
Dr. Stefan Stangaciu, MD, Acupuncturist, Apitherapist, and Apiphytotherapist
E-mail: drstangaciu@gmail.com and drstangaciu@apitherapy.com
http://www.apitherapy.com/index.php/eng/About-us

Reverse Tweezers
Amazon.com

Lyme Disease Forum
Healing Lyme with Bee Venom
https://www.facebook.com/groups/892134647496039/

Physicians
Klinghardt Academy
Contact: Debbie Floyd
2 Orchard Way
Warren, NH 07059
1-989-899-1650
info@klinghardtacademy.com
http://www.klinghardtacademy.com/lyme-disease/

Bradford S. Weeks, M.D.
Whidbey Island, State of Washington
Founder, and President Emeritus, America Apitherapy Society
Phone: 360-341-2303   Email: brad@alternativehealthadvocates.com
www.weeksmd.com / www.eattheseed.com / www.safalab.com
YouTube videos available at: BradWeeksMD

Herbs
Mountain Rose Herbs
https://www.mountainroseherbs.com/

Propolis
Holistic Herb Solutions
http://www.holisherb.com/bee-propolis-powder/

Documents

Before I even think of working with anyone with BVT, they must fill out the *Informed Consent to Apitherapy* form. It explains what BVT apitherapy and what each can expect from the other. If they wish a copy, I will give them one. Although, I have found that those seeking alternative healing methods allow the ethical mind to extend to other avenues of their lives. What this means is that they trust me to know what I'm doing and I don't usually worry about lawsuits.

They also fill the 8-page *Friend's Personal History*. We will not even discuss BVT until I have that document in my hand and they are sitting on the table in front of me. I go over each question and ask questions if I don't understand their responses or hand writing. While going over the questionnaire, other questions will arise based on the responses. By the time the 2-3 hours is over, I know the person well enough and we have established a bond of trust. At the same time, I always answer their questions, easing their minds. Trust is crucial between you and the BVT recipient.

You will find these documents on the following pages. Use them with my permission and change them according to your methods and/or practice.

Informed Consent to Apitherapy

Apitherapy is the art and science of making therapeutic use of products of the honeybee hive, including honey, pollen, propolis, royal jelly, apilarnil, beeswax, and bee venom. To be most effective the treatment requires a relationship of trust and confidence between Apitherapist and the Recipient of Apitherapy. Both parties must recognize the need to cooperate and work together.

I, _____ the recipient, understand that:

- ✓ Apitherapy is not a procedure approved by the US Food and Drug Administration, the American Medical Association, or any other regulatory agency in the United States.
- ✓ Apitherapy address the whole body, including mind and spirit, in a holistic way.
- ✓ There are no clearly established protocols for Apitherapy.
- ✓ Complications of Apitherapy can include itching, swelling, bruising, infection, temporary discomfort and allergic reactions ranging from skin irritation or rash up to anaphylactic shock which can cause difficulty breathing, loss of consciousness and even death if not treated appropriately.
- ✓ The Apitherapist has made no guarantees or promises of any kind regarding the safety, efficacy, or results of Apitherapy.
- ✓ Alternatives to Apitherapy may include surgery, medication, massage, spinal manipulation, medical treatment and advice, and a regimen of diet and exercise. All have been considered or tried and I have chosen to pursue Apitherapy for relieving pain, enhancing well-being, and/or improving my physical condition.

I have given the Apitherapist a clear, candid, and complete disclosure of my medical history including problems, treatments, and medications. I am not on Beta-blockers. Should I begin to exhibit signs of a significant allergic reaction. I authorize the Apitherapist to administer Epinephrine and/or an antihistamine.

The Apitherapist has advised me of the procedure planned. I have received a clear, comprehensive explanation of the risks inherent in Apitherapy procedures and their possible adverse consequences, including death. I have discussed these matters with the Apitherapist, and am satisfied that the answers have been understandable, thorough, and have adequately addressed my concerns. I am confident I have the information necessary to understand the risks and benefits of the procedure so I may give this informed consent. I understand that I am entitled to receive a copy of this consent form when it is executed.

I, _____, the Apitherapist, stated that I have fully and frankly explained the risks and benefits of Apitherapy, and pledge my best efforts to administer it in a proper manner based on my training, experience, and best judgement.

We, the Apitherapist and Recipient, understand the cooperative nature of this treatment and understand our individual and each other's responsibilities. We have read and understood this document, affirm the statements made above, and evidence our acceptance of the above terms by signing below.

Signed this _____day of _____, year of _____, at _____

_____   _____
Recipient   Apitherapist

Personal History

Date:_____

Name:_____ Age:_____ DOB:_____

Address:_____

Phone:_____Cell:_____Work:_____

Height:_____ Weight:_____ 1 year ago:_____ 5 years ago: _____

Occupation:_____ Full time:_____ Part Time:_____

Living situation: Alone _____ Friends ____ Partner ____ Spouse ____ Parents ____ Children ____ Pets ____

Name of your physician:_____

Physician's Address:_____ Phone:_____

Please list any other providers you are currently working with:_____

_____

_____

Please list any current health conditions diagnosed by a medical doctor:_____

_____

_____

When was your last physical exam:_____

Family History: Please describe any relevant or major health related issues: cancer, mental illnesses, diabetes, heart disease, etc.
Mother:_____

Father:_____

Sister(s):_____

Brother(s):_____

Maternal Grandmother: _____

Maternal Grandfather: _____

Paternal Grandmother:_____

Paternal Grandfather: _____

Medical History: List all major health problems including any surgeries/operations:
<u>**Problem:**</u>   *Year*

_____

_____

_____

_____

_____

_____

_____

_____

Please list all medications you are taking including aspirin, antacids, etc. and if they are Over-the-Counter or prescription, indicating dosage and frequency:_____

_____

_____

_____

_____

_____

Please list all herbs, vitamins, and dietary supplements you are presently taking indicating dosage and frequency:_____

_____

_____

_____

_____

_____

_____

List all known foods, herbs, supplements, medications, and environmental factors to which you have a known allergy:_____

_____

_____

_____

_____

_____

What are your major health concerns and intentions for your visit today: _____

_____

_____

_____

Dietary Information: Describe below your typical meals. Please be as specific as possible. For example, instead of "oil", note type of oil, such as olive, corn, etc. Instead of "bread" list whether white or whole grain, etc. Instead of "vegetables" list the type of vegetable, how prepared, canned, frozen, or fresh, etc. Please include al beverages, type and quantity, like 2 cups of orange juice, 1 cup of coffee, etc.

Breakfast:

_____

_____

_____

_____

_____

Morning snack(s):

_____

_____

_____

Lunch:

_____

_____

_____

_____

_____

Afternoon snack(s):

_____

_____

Dinner:

_____

_____

_____

_____

_____

Daily water consumption - number of glasses/day:_____

List any recurring food cravings, such as salt, starch, sugar, chocolate, etc. Please list as many as applicable including times of day or month_____

_____

_____

GENERAL HEALTH

Cardiovascular and Throat

____ High blood pressure
____ Low blood pressure
____ Pain in heart
____ Poor circulation
____ Swelling
____ Stroke/murmur

Respiratory

____ Chest pain
____ Difficulty breathing
____ Cough
____ Tuberculosis
____ Congestion
____ Itchy ears/eyes
____ Asthma
____ Coughing up blood

Skin

____ Boils
____ Bruises
____ Dryness
____ Itching
____ Varicose veins
____ Skin eruptions

Urinary/Kidney

____ Excessive urination
____ Water retention
____ Burning urine
____ Kidney stones
____ Lower back pain
____ Wheezing
____ Circles under eyes
____ Blood in urine

Muscles/Joints

____ Backache
____ Broken bones
____ Limited mobility
____ Arthritis
____ Bursitis
____ Weakness

Gastro-Intestinal

____ Belching
____ Colitis
____ Constipation
____ Abdominal pain
____ Liver disorders
____ Gallstones
____ Ulcers

Eyes, Ears, Nose,

____ Ear aches
____ Hay fever
____ Sore throat
____ Canker sores
____ Eye pains
____ Sinus infections
____ Tonsils
____ Nosebleeds
____ Failing vision
____ Sinus congestion
____ Hearing loss
___Difficulty breathing

General

____ Fatigue
____ Excessive thirst
____ Difficulty sleeping
____ Night sweats
____ Loss of appetite
____ Irritability
____ Fever
____ Always hungry
____ Cold hands/feet

Male Reproductive

____ Digestive troubles	____ Burning/discharge	____ Painful testicles
____ Testicles - lumps, swelling	____ Vasectomy	

Female Reproductive

Age of first period: ____

____ Heavy bleeding	____ Breast lumps	____ Vaginal discharge
____ Genital herpes	____ Painful intercourse	____ PMS
____ Breast pain	____ Pre-menopausal	____ Infertility
____ Menopause	____ Mood Swings	____ Pains/cramps
____ Irregular cycles	____ Pelvic pain	____ Blood clots
____ Anemia	____ Vaginal itching	____ Hot flashes
____ Vaginal dryness	____ Not able to conceive	

Contraceptive/Pregnancy History

____ Birth Control Pills	____ Rhythm-method	____ I.U.D.
____ Diaphragm	____ Condoms	____ Mucous-method
____ Cervical Cap	____ Spermicides	____ Fertility lens

Please list each pregnancy you have had, including miscarriages:_____

_____

_____

CURRENT STATE OF EMOTIONS AND SPIRITUAL WELL-BEING

Please check all those that describe you:

____ I am often not able to express my emotions.
____ I am dissatisfied with my job.
____ I am often stressed out and not able to cope properly.
____ Even though I am in a relationship, I often feel lonely.
____ I often feel anxious and nervous for no good reason.
____ I don't sleep well at night and have a hard time waking up in the morning.
____ I often suffer from bad dreams and nightmares.
____ There are many things I'd like to change in my life. I just don't have the means.
____ I have very low energy and often feel exhausted mentally and physically
____ I don't enjoy my work and would rather be doing something else.
____ I find my children irritating and hard to relate to.
____ I have very few hobbies.
____ I often feel depressed for no reason.
____ I often become angry with people and feel guilty about it later.
____ I have a hard time letting go of the past.
____ I don't look towards the future with much enthusiasm.
____ I am not able to concentrate for extended periods of time.
____ My outlook is more negative than positive.
____ I spend a great deal of time worrying about what people think about me.

____ I tend to see the good in people
____ I have a great sense of humor and love a good joke.

____ I receive great joy from my family.

____ My outlook on life is positive.

____ My job uses all of my greatest talent.

____ I have plenty of energy to do all the things I want.

____ I sleep well at night and feel rested in the morning,.

____ I can concentrate on the task at hand for as long as it takes.

____ I have a strong spiritual faith.

____ I am able to express anger constructively.

____ I practice meditation or other relaxation techniques.

____ I try to maintain peace of mind and tranquility.

____ I have many close friends that I can always count on.

____ I accept full responsibility for my actions.

____ I trust my intuition and believe that things happen for a reason.

____ I do not harbor any resentment from the past.

____ I can feel completely fulfilled even if I'm alone.

____ I have many hobbies and interests to keep me preoccupied.

____ How I view myself is more important than how others seen me.

____ I often go out of my way to help others.

Please list approximate dates and describe the nature of any traumatic experiences you have had in the past 7 years (divorce, surgery, end of a relationship, loss of job, change of residence, injury, death of a loved one, etc.)

Year   Event

_____

_____

_____

_____

_____

LIFESTYLE HABITS

Do you engage in regular physical activity   ____Yes ____ No

If, for how many minutes? _____ How Often? _____

Do you smoke tobacco?   ____Yes ____ No

If yes, how much? _____

Do you drink alcohol?   ____Yes ____ No

If yes, how much? _____ How often? _____

Do you drink coffee and/or caffeinated beverages?   ____Yes ____ No

If yes, how much? _____ How often? _____

How many hours of television do you watch in a week? _____

Do you use artificial sweeteners?   ____Yes ____ No

Please use this space to add any other information about yourself that you think will be helpful:

_____

_____

_____

_____

COMMENTS AND SUGGESTIONS FOR FRIEND

Dietary suggestions:

_____

_____

_____

_____

_____

_____

_____

Recommended herbs and nutrients including dosage:

_____

_____

_____

_____

_____

_____

_____

_____

Lifestyle modification changes:

_____

_____

_____

_____

_____

_____

Relaxation techniques and exercises:

_____

_____

_____

_____

Other suggestions:

_____

_____

_____

_____

_____

The BEe Healing Guild is a non-profit organization for the purpose of:

- Having a Gathering to create a space for like-minded individuals to share, experience, teach, learn, express, guide, experience, heal, and understand the components of body, mind, and spirit for the sake of and for honeybees, humans, and Mother Earth.

- Teach BEe Perspective Beekeeping, a no-treatment method, and to certify individuals as teachers who will teach the BEe Perspective Beekeeping. In turn we will help fund, either partially or fully, the certified teachers of organizations teaching children and young adults.

- Bringing awareness to the global community regarding the honeybee crisis and bring them back to the basics of grass root beekeeping.

May you honor your honeybees as you honor your life! They give you 84% of your food. They are the only creatures that give you everything including their lives for your health and well-being. All they ask as that you treat them with humaneness.

BEe loved,
Lady Spirit Moon
Beekeeper

BEe Healing Guild
Lady@BEeHealing.buzz
www.BEeHealing.buzz

CPSIA information can be obtained
at www.ICGtesting.com
Printed in the USA
BVOW05s0328280517

485119BV00036B/547/P